Meadowvale School

A Hundred Circling Camps

KEYS TO READING

the watch-fires of

a hundred circling camps

JULIA WARD HOWE

Louise Matteoni

Wilson H. Lane

Floyd Sucher

Versie G. Burns

Theodore L. Harris, *Advisory Author*

Harold B. Allen, *Linguistic Consultant*

THE ECONOMY COMPANY   Oklahoma City   Indianapolis   Orange, CA

Design: James Stockton

Cover Illustration: Jon Goodell

ISBN 0-8332-1298-2

THE ECONOMY COMPANY, Educational Publishers
1901 North Walnut   Oklahoma City, Oklahoma 73125

Contents

From Where You Stand

Hand in Hand

More Than One Way

Side Ways

Inside Out

Touch the Sky

From Where You Stand

Sparkle and Struggle

An audience sees only the glitter and excitement of a circus performance. But there is another side to the circus. From where you stand, can you see the hard work, courage, and skill that go into a circus act?

Being in a circus act isn't all fun. Few jobs require so much time and hard work. The brief minutes that an act appears in the circus ring follow long hours, weeks, months, and even

years of practice. Both bravery and effort must be used to build the strength and skill which make the circus exciting for the performers and for the audience.

Swing to Danger

Louisa Prince

Danger is always with the trapeze artists in a circus. In this story the circus performers live in a children's home. Carmen and Dolores perform together on the high wire, but they are not friends. But the way the girls see each other changes when one dangerous mistake on the trapeze almost costs Carmen her life.

"Carmen," called Dolores. "Are you sure you've spent enough time on the swings? I don't want to be blamed if you slip and fall off the trapeze tomorrow."

"I don't need any practice," said Carmen. "I'm strong, and I'm good. I'm the best flier here, and you know it. Just be sure your hands don't slip when you catch me, that's all."

Dolores remembered how she had felt when she first came to Barriéntez. She had been so alone, but at the same time, so angry at everything around her. She forced herself not to say something mean to Carmen.

Carmen was the new girl at Barriéntez. Her parents had been killed in an automobile accident three months ago. At first, Carmen had worked hard to learn her circus act. She had worked as though nothing else mattered. Then, suddenly, she had stopped working. It was true that Carmen was good, but everyone needs to practice. Carmen didn't seem to think so. The safety nets usually caught anyone who fell from the trapeze. Still, Dolores thought, Carmen is taking a dangerous chance by not practicing.

After practice, Dolores walked to dinner behind Carmen and some of Carmen's friends. They were laughing and talking happily. But Carmen kept glancing back over her shoulder at Dolores. Was Carmen afraid? Dolores wondered. Perhaps she was only acting brave.

During dinner, everyone was more noisy than usual. This often happened the night before a show. People shouted at each other across the room. Two boys in the food line started pushing each other. Mr. Rodriguez, one of the house fathers, had to separate them. The dining room buzzed with excitement.

The afternoon of the show was sunny and bright. Everyone seemed more at peace than they had the evening before. The grand parade was almost over. The five girls in the trapeze act

were getting ready to perform. Carmen turned angry eyes toward Dolores. "Be sure you put enough rosin on your hands," she said. "I would hate for you to let anyone slip."

Again, Dolores forced herself not to answer. What was Carmen trying to prove?

A moment later a voice boomed from the center ring. "Ladies and gentlemen, the circus presents the Shooting Stars." Carmen, Dolores, Elaine, Margaret, and Amelia ran to the center of the ring. They bowed and waved to the crowd. Then they hurried to the ropes.

Four of the girls climbed the rope ladder to their platform at one end of the ring. Dolores, the catcher, climbed another ladder to her trapeze at the other end.

The music started. Elaine grabbed the trapeze bar. She matched its swing to Dolores's. When the time was right, she leaped from the platform and flew high into the air. At exactly the right moment, she let go of the bar and stretched to reach Dolores's hands. Perfect. Dolores felt a tug on her shoulders. She swung Elaine, first backward, and then toward Elaine's own trapeze. Elaine caught the bar, swung, and landed lightly on the platform. She bowed and waved as the crowd clapped.

Next it was Carmen's turn. Carmen grabbed the bar and sent the trapeze flying out from the platform. When the bar swung back, she leaped out into the air, caught the bar, and flipped upside down to hang by her feet. On her next swing she would reach out to take Dolores's hands.

Something was wrong. Dolores could see that Carmen wasn't going to make it. "Carmen, no!" she cried. "Your timing is off. You can't reach me!"

Carmen tried anyway. Dolores stretched, but couldn't reach Carmen's outstretched arms. The trapeze swung away, carrying

Carmen with it. Carmen was now hanging dizzily from the bar by one foot. She could not move. One of the ropes was twisted around her foot.

Screaming with pain, Carmen hung in the air. Now Carmen swayed slowly, just out of Dolores's reach.

The crowd was standing now, straining to see the two girls.

Quickly, Dolores began to swing back and forth. She pulled harder and harder. She could see Carmen's face turning red. With all her might, Dolores pulled her body forward to reach Carmen's trapeze.

Dolores dropped to hang by her feet. The extra body length would put her closer to Carmen. Now she was so close that she could see the tears of pain on Carmen's face. She gathered her strength, reached for the bar, and missed.

The crowd screamed as Dolores's hands grabbed at the air. Dolores had felt herself start to slip. She fought hard to pull herself back up into a sitting position.

With shaking hands, Dolores wiped the sweat from her eyes. She wasn't thinking about herself now. Carmen's cries of pain drowned out all other thoughts.

Dolores began to swing back and forth again. She had missed the bar once. She would have to try even harder. The ropes groaned as she swung closer and closer to Carmen. All Dolores could hear was her own heart pounding and Carmen's cries of pain.

Again, Dolores dropped to hang by her feet. But still the other trapeze was just out of reach. She had to try harder. As her swing reached its peak, Dolores gave a sharp cry. One of her feet had slipped! Her trapeze began to jerk and swing wildly. Dolores fought to keep her balance. At the last moment she snapped her body up with the other foot. She grabbed her bar with both hands.

She caught her breath and tried to stay calm. Down below, the crowd was hushed.

Dolores worked steadily to get control of her trapeze again. It slowed to a gentle sway. A feeling of calmness began to come over her.

"Hold on, Carmen," said Dolores. "I'll be right there." She gave a mighty effort and on her next swing reached out and grabbed Carmen's trapeze. She sat on it and then spoke quietly to Carmen. "Pull your body up and grab the bar. I'm going to free your foot."

"I can't," moaned Carmen. "I'm not strong enough. Get me down from here. I think my ankle is broken!"

"Carmen, I can't help you unless you help yourself," said Dolores. "You have to pull yourself up. You told me yesterday that you were strong. You said that you were the best flier here. Now prove it! Show me!"

Carmen groaned as she clenched her teeth and tried to pull herself up. Again and again she tried. Again and again she fell back. The crowd groaned each time. Then, with all her might, Carmen jerked forward and wrapped her fingers around the bar. Dolores reached over and untwisted the rope from Carmen's foot. Carmen was free.

"Carmen," said Dolores quietly, "I can't swing both of us. You're going to have to pull."

"I can't move!" cried Carmen. "I told you before. I think my ankle is broken."

"You have to move," said Dolores. "If you fall now, you could really hurt yourself."

The trapeze was swinging closer and closer to the platform. Soon it was only inches away.

"Carmen, on the next swing, reach for the platform," said Dolores. "Use your good foot."

With one last pull the girls swung themselves toward the platform. Elaine, Margaret, and Amelia pulled them quickly onto the platform. They were safe. As they began to climb carefully down the rope ladder, the crowd cheered wildly. Elaine and Margaret helped Carmen down, one step at a time.

Later, while the doctor at the hospital was putting the cast on Carmen's ankle, he looked up and smiled. "It looks like you're going to be helping the younger children until this cast comes off, Carmen."

"How long will it be before I can fly again?" asked Carmen.

Dolores had walked into the room just in time to hear Carmen's question. "Not until your cast comes off, like the doctor said. You're heavy enough to catch, anyway," said Dolores. "With that cast on your ankle, you'd pull me right off my trapeze."

Carmen smiled and held out her hand to Dolores. "Dolores, thanks for saving me. I'll never be able to help you as much as you helped me."

"Oh, yes, you can," laughed Dolores. "Don't get any heavier while you're sitting around."

Laughter bubbled through the room as Dolores and Carmen hugged each other.

Think About This:

1. What gave Carmen the idea that she didn't need to practice?
2. How would Dolores have felt if she had been unable to reach Carmen?
3. How did Carmen and Dolores feel about each other after the accident?

Backstage on Clown Alley

Patricia Schoch

Most people who watch a circus see only the excitement and sparkle. But backstage, on Clown Alley, a circus has a different feel. Clown Alley is a very special place where clowns put on makeup and costumes. Steve LaPorte is a clown. From backstage, on Clown Alley, what does he see?

A sudden quiet falls over the crowd. The lights go down. A blazing drumroll begins.

"LADIES AND GENTLEMEN, CHILDREN OF ALL AGES, . . ." booms a voice. The hushed crowd turns to see the ringmaster. "WELCOME TO RINGLING BROTHERS AND BARNUM AND BAILEY CIRCUS . . ."

Before the show, Steve LaPorte quickly straps stilts to his feet. He becomes the thirteen-foot-tall clown who leads the grand parade.

Steve walks like a giant. Feathers wave from his hat. His green hair bounces with every step. He waves to show the crowd all the circus acts coming in behind him.

After the parade, Steve goes to a ladder. He sits on top of it and takes off the stilts. Then he hurries to change for his next act.

When Steve decided to be a clown, he wrote to the circus's Clown College in Venice, Florida. He was one of forty-eight people chosen.

The clowning course took eight weeks. Steve studied things like exercises, cooking, making faces, stilt walking, and tumbling. Clowns must be able to make their own outfits. They must also know how to make their own hair pieces.

At the end of eight weeks, Steve was one of twenty people chosen to work in the circus. He worked with the circus for a year. Then he taught in the Clown College.

Among Steve's best pupils was a lively girl named Terri. Before the winter was over, Steve and Terri were married. Terri

was given a job as a clown with the circus. Steve became the boss clown. He was very young to be a boss clown.

Steve and Terri work together. Their home for most of the year is a room in the circus train. They do their own cooking in a kitchen on the train.

The clowns, along with the other circus people, all live on the same train. Because they are together so much, they are like one big family.

The circus moves on Monday and Tuesday, and the show opens on Wednesday. Steve sometimes groans, "Fourteen shows this week, then pack up and move on."

A circus day begins about ten in the morning. Steve likes to see the sights in a new city early in the day. Then, at one o'clock, he heads for Clown Alley to get ready for the show. This takes about

an hour. The circus people do two or three shows a day. They have just an hour between shows.

The life of a circus clown can be hard. While the clowns aren't performing, they are trying out new acts. They always work to make the show better. But the hard work doesn't matter when people show the clowns that they love them.

Because circus people move around a lot, they have few friends outside the circus. It makes Steve happy when children run out and hand him a letter they've written or a picture of a clown they've drawn. Some even say they love him.

Terri has made up her own clown act. She likes the circus as much as Steve does. They both feel that the circus is real show business, just like the theater. Steve once said, "The circus gives people a way to get away from their troubles. That, to me, makes it very important."

Rhymes into Riddles

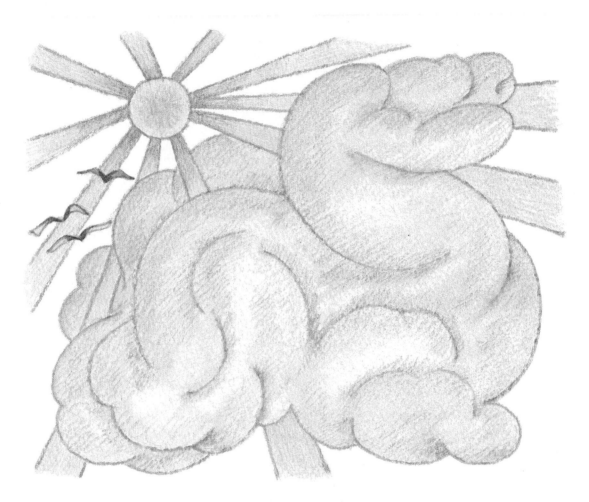

Here is a riddle: What can look like a face, a ship, or a dragon as it floats by? The answer is a cloud. Riddles can help you to see some surprises in everyday things. Poetry can do the same thing. Read these poems as riddles and tell what you see by guessing their subjects and titles.

My body a rounded stone
with a pattern of smooth seams.
My head a short snake,
retractive, projective.
My legs come out of their sleeves
or shrink within,
and so does my chin.
My eyelids are quick clamps.

My back is my roof.
I am always at home.
I travel where my house walks.
It is a smooth stone.
It floats within the lake,
or rests in the dust.
My flesh lives tenderly
inside its bone.

May Swenson

He clasps the crag with crooked hands;
Close to the sun in lonely lands,
Ring'd with the azure world, he stands,

The wrinkled sea beneath him crawls;
He watches from his mountain walls,
And like a thunderbolt he falls.

Alfred, Lord Tennyson

A shadow is floating through the moonlight.
Its wings don't make a sound.
Its claws are long, its beak is bright.
Its eyes try all the corners of the night.
It calls and calls: all the air swells and heaves
And washes up and down like water.

Randall Jarrell

In the gray evening
I see a long green serpent
With its tail in the dahlias.

It lies in loops across the grass
And drinks softly at the faucet.

I can hear it swallow.

Beatrice Janosco

Think About This:

1. The titles of three of the poems are "Living Tenderly," "The Eagle," and "The Garden Hose." Did you guess any of these titles?
2. What words in the first poem were used to describe the turtle's shell? Its skin?
3. In the second poem, what do you think it might mean for an eagle to fall "like a thunderbolt"?
4. The third poem is untitled. What is it describing? In what ways is it like the second poem?
5. Why do you think the garden hose was compared to a snake in the fourth poem?

27

Fox at Midnight _____

Betsy Byars

    At first Tom did not like the idea of spending his summer at Aunt Millie's farm. But Tom began to see things differently when he saw a beautiful black fox running through the grass. This story begins near the end of Tom's summer.

We went into the house and I said to Uncle Fred, "What are you going to do with the baby fox?"

"That's my bait. Every hunter alive's got some way to get a fox. They got some special trap or something. Mr. Baynes down at the store makes up a special mixture that he says foxes can't resist. My way is to set up a trap, using the baby fox for bait. I'll sit out on the back porch tonight and watch for her."

"Oh."

"It never fails. This is one bait a fox can't resist."

"Are you getting sick?" Aunt Millie asked at supper that night.

"I guess I'm a little tired."

"Well, I should think so! Helping with the pump out in the broiling sun all morning and then tracking that fox all afternoon. It's a wonder you don't have heatstroke. You eat something though, hear? You have to keep up your strength."

"I'm just not hungry."

"It's the heat. But, listen, you drink your tea. You *will* have heatstroke sure enough if you let your body get dried out."

I finished my tea and went up to my room. I did not even look out the window, because I knew I could see the rabbit hutch by the garage, and I never again wanted to see that baby fox cowering against the wall.

Hazeline came out of her room and looked in at me on the bed. "You feeling better?"

I nodded. She was all dressed up now in a blue dress she had made for 4-H. Her face looked good, as if letting it get swollen had been beneficial. I knew she was going downstairs to sit on the porch and wait for Mikey. I knew he would come, too. One time Petie and I had had the worst argument in the world. We were just sitting on the steps one afternoon and Petie had been thinking in silence for a while and then he said, "I wonder what I'll look like when I'm grown."

And I said, "Porky Pig." I don't know why I said that, because I wasn't mad at him or anything. And he said, "Well, that's better than looking like Daffy Duck." And I said, "Meaning *I* look like Daffy Duck?" And he said, "Yes, around the mouth." And then we both got angry and started screaming things and I thought our friendship was over, only two days later it was just like it had never happened.

"Mikey will come over," I said.

"Who cares? I don't care if I never see him again," she said, twisting her fingers in her pearls. He had given her those when she had graduated from high school two months ago.

"I know, but I bet he comes anyway."

"Well, I can't stop him of course. It's a free country."

"Hazeline?"

"What?"

"You know that fox I was telling you about? The black one?"

"Sure."

"Well, your dad has her baby out in the rabbit hutch and he's going to shoot her."

"I know it. I heard. But, listen, don't let it upset you, hear?"

"Hazeline, I don't want anything to happen to that fox."

"Tommy, listen, all wild animals die in some violent way. It's their life. Wild animals just don't die of old age. They get killed by an enemy or by the weather or they have an accident or they get rabies or some other disease or they get shot. That's the way nature is."

"I know that," I said quickly, because I did not want to hear any more.

"You just forget the fox. Tomorrow maybe we can go to the picture show in Clinton or something."

"All right."

She went down the steps then and out onto the porch, and I could hear the swing begin to creak.

I got up and went down the steps and walked to the tree in front of the rabbit hutch. I could not explain why I did this. I didn't want to see the baby fox again, and yet here I was.

He did not see me. He was busy biting the wires of his cage with great fury and determination. I could hear the clicking of his sharp tiny teeth against the wire, but he was making no progress. Then he stopped. He still had not seen me, but he had heard or smelled something, and he raised his head and let out a short cry. He waited; then after a moment he began biting the wires again.

I remained by the tree watching him, listening for the quavering cry that he uttered from time to time.

"Don't get your fingers in the cage," Uncle Fred warned behind me. "He may not be able to cut wire yet, but he sure could hurt a finger."

"All right."

"In a bit, when it starts getting dark, you can sit up here with me and watch for the fox."

A car came slowly up the drive, and I said to Uncle Fred, "It's Mikey."

Behind him in the doorway Aunt Millie said, "Did you say it's Mikey, Tom?"

I nodded.

"Praise be."

I walked around the front of the house and stood there for a minute. Mikey had not gotten out of the car but was sitting with one arm out the window, looking at Hazeline on the porch.

"What you doing?" he asked.

"Not much of anything," she said. "Just fighting the heat."

"You don't look hot — you look real good and cool."

"Sometimes looks are deceiving."

He ran his fingers over the steering wheel. There was a pause; then he said, "Do you want to ride up to the lake?"

"I don't know."

"When you going to make up your mind?"

"I just don't know whether I feel like looking at boats racing all over creation tonight."

"Do you want to go for a ride?"

"I don't know."

"I'll give you" — he looked at his watch — "one minute to make up your mind."

He started watching the seconds tick off, and I held up my watch too and counted, and only eleven seconds had gone by when Hazeline got up and said, "I'll go," and started laughing. "Tell Mom I'm going off with Mikey," she said over her shoulder and got in the car.

I went into the kitchen where Aunt Millie was standing in front of the electric fan and said, "Hazeline has gone off with Mikey."

I heard the cry of the baby fox again, and I thought I would be hearing that sound forever. One time Petie Burkis fell down and broke his leg on the school playground and he said, "Oh!" in this real terrible, painful way, and I never could forget it. Later I tried to make him say it again that same way, and one whole afternoon Petie did nothing but say the word *Oh* over and over — a thousand times maybe — and in all those thousand tries, he never sounded that same way again. I still remember it though, exactly, like I will always remember the way that baby fox sounded when he cried.

It seemed to get dark quickly that night. Uncle Fred was already out on the back porch. He had brought out a chair and was sitting with his gun beside him, pointing to the floor. I never saw anyone sit any quieter. You wouldn't have noticed him at all he was so still.

I stood beside him inside the screen door. Through the screen I could see the tiny fox lift his black nose and cry again. Now, for the first time, there was an answer — the bark of his mother.

I looked toward the garden, because that's where the sound had come from, but Uncle Fred did not even turn his head. In a frenzy now that he had heard his mother, the baby fox moved about the cage, pulling at the wire and crying again and again.

Just then there was the sound of thunder from the west, a long rolling sound, and Aunt Millie came to the door beside me and said, "Bless me, is that thunder?" She looked out at the sky. "Was that thunder, Fred?"

"Could be," he said without moving.

"Look!" Aunt Millie said. "I swear I see black clouds. You see, Tom?"

"Yes'm."

"And feel that breeze. Honestly, when you think you have

reached absolutely the end of your endurance, then the breeze comes. I could not have drawn one more breath of hot air, and now we are going to have a storm."

We stood in the doorway, feeling the breeze, forgetting for a moment the baby fox.

Then I saw Uncle Fred's gun rise ever so slightly in the direction of the fence behind the garage. I could not see any sign of the fox, but I knew that she must be there. Uncle Fred would not be wrong.

The breeze quickened, and abruptly the dishpan which Aunt Millie had left on the porch railing clattered to the floor. For the first time Uncle Fred turned his head and looked in annoyance at the pan and then at Aunt Millie.

"Did it scare your fox off?" she asked.

He nodded, then shifted in the chair and said, "She'll be back."

In just a short time the sky to the west had gotten black as ink. Low on the horizon, forks of lightning streaked the sky.

"Now, Fred, don't you sit out here while it's thundering and lightning. I mean it. No fox is worth getting struck by lightning for."

He nodded, and she turned to me and said, "You come on and help me shut the windows. Some of those upstairs are stuck wide open. Just hit them with the heel of your hand on the side till you can get them down."

I started up the stairs and she said again, "Fred, come on in when it starts storming. That fox'll be back tomorrow night, too."

I went upstairs and started hitting the sides of the windows. I had just gotten one window to jerk down about two inches when I heard the gunshot. I had never heard any worse sound in my life. It was a very final sound, like the most enormous period in the world. Bam. Period. The end.

I ran out of my room and down the steps so fast I could not even tell you how many times my feet touched the stairs, none maybe. I went out the back door, opening it so fast I hit the back of Uncle Fred's chair. I looked toward the rabbit hutch, said, "Where?"

then looked at the back fence. Then I looked down at Uncle Fred, who was doing something with his gun.

"Missed," he said.

Suddenly I felt weak. My legs were like two pieces of rope, like that trick that Hindu magicians do when they make rope come straight up out of a basket and then say a magic word and make the rope collapse. My legs felt like they were going to collapse at any second. I managed to force these two pieces of rope to carry me up the stairs and into the room.

I closed two windows, and the third one, in sympathy perhaps, just banged down all by itself. Then I sank to the bed.

I had no intention of going to sleep when I lay down on the bed; I did not think I would ever be able to sleep again, but that is what I did. I fell right asleep and did not even move until four hours later when I awoke. It was one o'clock in the morning.

The storm was in full force, or perhaps it was a second storm, but the house was quiet. I got up and went out into the hall. I could not hear anything but the sound of the rain and Hazeline's transistor radio, which was sputtering with static beside her on the pillow.

I went down the stairs, one by one. I did not make a sound. I stepped on the part of the steps near the wall because Petie had told me that was how burglars got up stairs unheard. I was just stepping into the hall, when without warning, the hall light went on. Aunt Millie was standing there in her bathrobe, squinting at me.

"What's wrong?" she asked.

"Nothing. I just didn't know what time it was."

"Well" — she looked closely at her watch — "it's just past one o'clock."

"I went to sleep in my clothes."

"Well, you get on your pajamas and get back to bed. This is the first good sleeping night we've had, and you mustn't let it go to waste."

"Sure."

"Well, go on back up the steps." She watched me go up two steps and then she said, "Goodness, we've gotten on so well all summer, I'd hate for anything to happen now right before your parents get home."

"Aunt Millie, did Uncle Fred get the fox?"

"No."

"Is he still out on the porch?"

"In this rain? No, he is fast asleep in his bed like you ought to be."

She waited until I was up the stairs and then she turned out the light. I went into my room and she called, "Are you getting in bed?"

I lay down. "Yes."

"And go to sleep."

I lay in bed for a long time, still in my clothes, and then I got up very carefully. I walked over to the window and looked out at the tree. Bubba and Fred Jr. used to just run up and down all the time like monkeys. I could imagine them climbing up, laughing and brown, racing, going out on all sorts of perilous limbs just to be first at the window. I opened the window, pushed out the screen, reached out into the rain, and felt for the smooth spot Aunt Millie had told me was worn into the bark of the tree.

I took off my shoes and knelt on the windowsill. There was an enormous flash of lightning that turned the whole world white for a moment, and then I climbed out onto the nearest branch and circled the trunk around with my arms.

I thought that I could never get one step farther. I thought that I could never move even one muscle or I would fall. I thought that in the morning when Aunt Millie came up to see why I wasn't at breakfast, she would find me here, pressed into the tree, still frozen with fear.

The rain was hard and slanting directly into my face. Finally I got up just enough courage to turn my face out of the rain. Then the lightning flashed again and I saw the ground about a million miles below. I held the tree so tightly the bark was cutting into my cheek.

I don't know how long I stayed that way. If I had tried to look at my watch, just that little movement would have thrown me off balance. After a while, though, I began to sort of slip down the tree. I never let go of the main trunk for a second. I just moved my arms downward in very small movements. Then, slowly, when I was practically kneeling on the first limb, I let my foot reach down for the next one.

If there were smooth spots on those branches, my feet never found them. They only touched one rough limb after another as, slowly, I kept inching down the tree, feeling my way, never looking down at the ground until, finally, my foot reached out for another limb and felt the cold wet grass. It shocked me for a moment and then I jumped down, landing on my hands and knees.

I got up and ran to the rabbit hutch. The baby fox was huddled in one corner of the pen where there was some shelter from the rain. The lightning flashed and I saw him watching me.

"I'm going to get you out," I said.

He crouched back farther in the hutch. In the next flash of lightning, I looked on the ground for a rock and I saw at my feet a small dead frog. I knew that the black fox in all this rain had brought that frog here to her baby. She was right now watching me somewhere.

There were bricks stacked in a neat pile under the hutch, and I took one and began to bang it against the lock. I was prepared to do this all night if necessary, but the lock was an old one and it opened right away.

The noise had scared the baby fox, and he was now making a whimpering sound. I unhooked the broken lock, opened the cage, and stepped back against the tree.

The baby fox did not move for a moment. I could barely see him, a small dark ball in the back of the cage. He waited, alert and suspicious, and then, after a moment, he moved in a crouch to the door of the cage. He cried sharply. From the bushes there was an answering bark.

He crouched lower. The lightning flashed again, and in that second he jumped and ran in the direction of the bushes. He barked as he ran. There was an immediate answer, and then only the sound of the rain. I waited against the tree, thinking about them, and then I heard the black fox bark one more time as she ran through the orchard with her baby.

And I thought, Someday I will be in a famous museum, walking along on the marble floors, looking at paintings. There will be one called "Blue Flowers" and I will look at that for a while, and the next one will be "Woman on the Beach" and I will look at that for a while, and then I will glance at the name of the next painting and it will be "Fox with Baby at Midnight," and I will look up and my heart will stop beating because there it will be, just the way it was this night, the black fox and her baby running beneath the wet ghostly apple trees toward a patch of light in the distance. And I thought, leaning against that tree in the rain, If there is a picture like that, I hope sometime I will get to see it.

Suddenly the rain began to slacken and I walked around the house. I had never been so wet in my life, and now that it was over, I was cold, too. And I was tired. I looked up at the tree, and there didn't seem to be any point in climbing back up when in just a few hours everyone would know what I had done anyway. I went up on the porch and rang the doorbell.

In all my life I have never felt so dumb and foolish as I did barefooted, soaking wet on that slick porch at two o'clock in the morning, waiting for someone to come and answer the door.

It was Aunt Millie in her cotton robe who turned on the porch light and peered out through the side windows at me.

I must have been an awful sight, like the poor little match girl, for she flung open the door at once and drew me in.

"What are you doing out there? What are you doing?"

"Who is it?" Uncle Fred asked as he came into the hall. He was pulling his pants up over his pajamas.

"It's Tom," Aunt Millie said.

"I meant who's at the door?"

"Tom," she said again.

"Tom?"

"Yes, he was just standing out there on the porch."

They both turned and looked at me, waiting for an explanation, and I cleared my throat and said, "Uncle Fred and Aunt Millie, I am awfully sorry but I have let the baby fox out of the rabbit hutch." I sounded very stiff and formal, and I thought the voice was a terrible thing to have to depend on, because I really did want them to know that I *was* sorry, and I didn't sound it in the least bit. I knew how much Uncle Fred had looked forward to the hunt and how important getting rid of the fox was to Aunt Millie, and I hated for them to be disappointed now.

There was a moment of silence. Then Aunt Millie said, "Why, that's perfectly all right, isn't it, Fred? Don't you think another thing about that. You just come on to bed. You're going to get pneumonia standing there in that puddle." She started for the linen closet. "I'll get you some towels."

Uncle Fred and I were left in the hall alone and I looked up at him and he looked like an enormous blue-eyed Indian.

"I'm sorry," I said again.

He looked at me and I knew he was seeing through all the very casual questions I had been asking all summer about foxes, and seeing through the long days I had spent in the woods. He was remembering the sorry way I had tried to keep him from finding the fox's den and the way I had looked when we did find it. I think all those pieces just snapped into place right then in Uncle Fred's mind, and I knew that if there was one person in the world who understood me it was this man who had seemed such a stranger.

He cleared his throat. "I never liked to see wild things in a pen myself," he said.

Aunt Millie came down the hall and threw a towel over my head and started rubbing. "Now get upstairs. I am not going to have you lying in bed with pneumonia when your mother arrives."

We went upstairs, she rubbing my head the whole way, me stumbling over the steps, and Hazeline calling from her room, "Who was that at the door?"

"Tom," Aunt Millie said.

"Who?"

"Me," I said.

"Oh."

We went into my room. "There," Aunt Millie exclaimed at the sight of my open window, "I knew it! I knew you'd be out there on that tree at the first opportunity." She shut the window with a bang. "There is no explaining a boy."

She turned down my bed, went out, and came back with a glass of milk.

"I'm sorry about your turkey and hen," I said.

"Oh, that! I bet you think I'm awful, carrying on the way I did."

"No."

"It was more the heat than anything else, like Fred said. Just don't think about it any more. That fox and her baby are miles away from here now, and they'll never come back to bother my birds. That's one thing about a fox. He learns."

She turned out the light, said, "It is starting to rain again. I declare we are going to be flooded out," and then went downstairs.

Think About This:

1. Why did Tom free the baby fox?
2. Why weren't Aunt Millie and Uncle Fred angry with Tom for freeing the baby fox?
3. What would you have done if you were in Tom's place when he freed the baby fox?

Lee Trevino

Evelyn M. Begley

As a young boy in Dallas, Texas, Lee Trevino probably only daydreamed about becoming a champion golfer. From where he stood, that dream looked like it might never come true. But it did, through a lot of hard work and practice.

"Boy, what a find!"

The brown-faced boy grabbed the golf club. He swung it round his head. To young Lee Trevino, who lived on the edge of the Dallas Glen Lakes Country Club, a golf club of his own was a dream come true. His dark eyes shining, Lee took a swing. That was the first swing of thousands. Today, Lee Trevino often hits over five hundred balls in a morning. The way he hits them has made him a top prize-winner in United States golf.

With that first golf club, Lee practiced hitting everything he could find. Then he got to know the son of the man who took care of the golf course. Lee asked the man, "Is it OK for me to use the course sometimes?"

After that he slipped over the fence often and played on real golfing ground. Then he ran home in the dark to the old house where he lived with his mother, grandfather, and two sisters.

When Lee was in the eighth grade, he had to quit school. His grandfather was not well. The family needed another income. Lee went to see Hardy Greenwood, a golf course owner nearby. He asked him for a job. Greenwood liked the look of the short, sturdy boy and hired him.

In his new job, Lee found himself man-of-all-work. As a caddie, he carried players' bags. But he also cleaned and helped take care of the greens and picked up balls. In between jobs he tried to improve his swing with a golf club.

"You got to hit the ball in this game until your hands bleed," Lee said years later. From the beginning he knew that working hard was the only way to win.

Most golf courses have eighteen holes. Lee Trevino played his first eighteen-hole round in a Dallas golf tournament when he was

fifteen. He didn't become famous, but it was a beginning. In four years he was a marine. He played golf all over the Far East.

"That's where I really learned to play," he says.

When he left the marines, Lee went back to work for Hardy Greenwood in Dallas. There he had fun playing golf with other people.

About this time Lee found a new trick. It turned out to be a trick that the crowds liked. He wrapped a large soda-pop bottle with tape and used it like a baseball bat to hit the golf ball. His strong arm sent the ball flying up to one hundred and fifty yards with this swing.

Brrrrr. . . . the alarm clock woke Lee up every morning for him to work out. Push-ups, sit-ups, then running through the sand to make his legs strong. All of this helped his game. In 1967 Lee's big break finally came.

"I didn't think it was worth it to pay $20 for the United States Open," Lee remembers. "But my wife, Claudia, did. She sent in the money."

Wearing loose pants and an old shirt, Lee walked into one of the best country clubs in the U.S. and went on to win $6000. He took fifth prize. But that $6000 moved him up from a $30-a-week job to partner at the Horizon Hills Golf Club. People were now following him in large groups to watch him play and to laugh at his jokes. ("Black is beautiful, but brown is cute.")

Golfer Arnold Palmer had fans called "Arnie's Army," but Lee was soon calling his fans "Lee's Fleas." The name stuck.

"I've got a lot of people cheering for me," Lee says, "because there are more poor people than rich people."

In 1968 Lee entered the Open Tournament at Oak Hill in Rochester, New York. Two people were playing against him —

Jack Nicklaus and Bert Yancey. All three scores were close together. In the first three rounds, Lee's scores were under par. That is, he finished the course with fewer strokes than were thought needed.

During the fourth round the crowd was wondering — would he crack? Would the tension be too much for him? Yancey was cool and quiet. Lee was cool, too. But he was talking a lot. At hole eleven, he sank a thirty-five-foot putt for a "birdie." That is, he finished with one swing less than par for that hole. Yancey had by that time played more than one "bogey." That is one swing more than par for the hole. Lee was now four swings ahead.

At hole eighteen, the crowd was silent for the last play. The sun shone down on Lee's arms as he made his swing. Twenty feet over the smooth green and into the cup. He had done it. Lee's Fleas roared. With that last play Lee Trevino had just broken the record at Oak Hill. He had become the first player to play all four rounds under par.

When he was handed his $30,000 check as prize money, Lee joked, "I'm going to buy the Alamo and give it back to Mexico."

In 1969 and 1970, Lee won many games, but in 1971, he won three important titles in four weeks. And he won more than $200,000 in prize money. Twice he sat down and wrote large checks to orphanages in towns where he played. He still gives away large sums of money in gifts.

In November, 1971, Lee Trevino was named Golfer of the Year by the Professional Golf Association. By the spring of 1974 he had earned eighteen titles and over one million dollars in prize money.

He's come a long way from the golf course where he first hit lost balls with a rusty club.

Ages and Ages of Ice Cream

Ben Watson

One of America's favorite foods is ice cream. But how much do you know about it? The following selection may show you some brand new ways of looking at ice cream.

The next time you get your lips around a smooth double dip of your favorite ice cream, give this a thought: ice cream has been around longer than cars or hamburgers or even the United States. In fact, this icy-sweet treat has its beginnings back almost two thousand years ago, maybe even before then.

Nero, a famous Roman emperor, would send teams of runners high up into the mountains of Italy to gather fresh snow. They would have to race back down to Rome with the snow before it melted. It was not an easy job, especially during the hot summer days. The snow was mixed in the emperor's kitchen with fruits and juices. Only Nero and his guests were able to enjoy this dessert, which was more like sherbet than ice cream.

When explorer Marco Polo traveled to the Orient, he found that the people there ate something like the Italian ices. The

Orientals would top off their meals with bowls of fruit and crushed ice. Sometimes they would add milk to this.

Years later, when Catherine de Medici married King Henry II of France, she took her own ice-cream makers with her to the court in Paris. The French palace went wild over this new dish. The king and his court decided they should keep this wonderful food all to themselves. The recipes were guarded like precious jewels. No one outside the palace could get even one lick.

At about the same time the French court was deciding on which flavor they liked the most, the king of England and his friends also were enjoying the chilly treat. So, not only was it a dish fit for a king — it was *only* for kings.

However, things changed. In the 1600s ice-cream shops were springing up all over England and France. Just about anyone was able to get a taste of ice cream at this time. People began making recipes of their own. In the late 1700s a new ice-cream dish was served in Italy — Biscuit Tortoni, which is still with us today. As you might have guessed, Tortoni was the name of the man who came up with this new style of ice cream. He spent most of his time inventing other new ways to make ice cream. The people packed into his shop to taste his latest dish.

About the same time Tortoni was dishing up his creamy inventions, a new country came into being across the ocean. The United States was very young when it got its first cold taste of ice cream. Ice cream was not served only to kings this time. Very important people like Thomas Jefferson and George Washington made it their favorite. Dolly Madison served it for dessert in the White House when her husband was president.

The first public ice-cream shop in America opened in New York City. The ice cream was cranked by hand, and the ice to help make it was hard to get. This made it cost a lot. There weren't too

many people who could pay the price very often. But this soon changed and more shops were scooping and selling the tasty stuff.

It was a man named Jacob Fussell who made this change happen. Fussell opened plants in 1851 that made more ice cream in less time with less work. It was still made by hand, but ice cream was easier to get. After several years, machines took over the making of ice cream. It then cost less and even more people were eating it.

There was now a flood of ice-cream shops and something new called the soda fountain. Some of these soda fountains were very fancy. People would flock into them on hot afternoons to

enjoy the ice cream and cold drinks. There were fizzy sodas with big scoops of strawberry or chocolate or cherry ice cream in them to delight the thirsty. Then someone invented the ice-cream sundae. But that wasn't quite enough. The banana split soon appeared in all its glory. Not even the kings of France and England when they had all the ice cream to themselves tasted anything like the wonder of this delight. Next came the biggest invention since Nero sent his swift slaves to the mountains for snow — the ice-cream cone. Everyone wanted one — or two — or more.

All sorts of new flavors were tried — pineapple, chocolate chip, marshmallow, and even bubble gum. Some of them lasted and are still here today. Some didn't — can you imagine radish ice cream? Or onion?

There was no question about it, Americans loved their ice cream. To supply all this ice cream, large companies — larger than Jacob Fussell's plants — were formed that did nothing but make ice cream. All the different companies have their own recipes. And they guard them almost as carefully as did the French kings. The companies hire people just to make up new flavors and improve on the old favorites. Ice cream making is a big business. More ice cream is eaten in America than anywhere else in the world. How do these companies make so much ice cream?

First comes the milk. It is brought to the ice-cream plant from the farm in those shiny tank trucks you may see on the highway. The raw milk is pumped from the tanks and the cream is separated from the milk. Then the two are mixed together in different amounts. Sugar is added to the whole thing and the result is called the "mix." Sometimes eggs are put into the "mix."

The mix is pasteurized, or heated, to kill any germs. Then sometimes the whole thing is homogenized. This means the fat in the milk and cream is broken down into small bits. Cooling is the next step. The mix gets thicker as it cools. Then it is time to add the flavorings, the nuts, and the fruit which go into the mix. The ice cream then is put in boxes which are stored in the freezing room. And it is cold there. The temperature is kept down to zero degrees Fahrenheit.

Now it is taken out of the boxes and put into smaller packages. Some of the ice cream is molded into ice-cream bars and other shaped treats. The packages that go to ice-cream stores for cones, sodas, and sundaes are larger than the ones in the grocery store. Finally the ice cream is loaded onto freezer trucks and is speeded to stores all over the country. The big ice-cream companies are careful about the way they make their ice cream and send it out. There are people at the companies who do nothing but test the ice cream to see that it is pure and fresh.

Most of the ice cream eaten today comes from these big plants, but you can still make your own ice cream at home. Maybe you have already. There are the old-fashioned hand-cranked freezers that make enough ice cream for a family. And there are smaller ones that use a motor run by electricity. Making ice cream can be a lot of fun, especially if you can get a big person to help you crank.

But whether you get your ice cream at a store or make it at home, it is still one of the greatest inventions of all time. Now, who do we thank for making ice cream possible, old ruler Nero or those rabbit-quick slaves with their icy hands full of snow? Either way, make mine a double dip of chocolate raisin and orange. You pick your own flavor.

Tonsils

Bill Cosby

Do you still have your tonsils? Bill Cosby doesn't. Bill thought that letting the doctor take his tonsils out would be fine, because then he could have all he wanted of his favorite food — ice cream! Read Bill's story to find out why he saw ice cream in a very different light without his tonsils.

I'll never forget the time I had a sore throat. Bad sore throat. And I said, "I have a sore throat."

And my mother said, "Let me feel your forehead." Mothers are always feeling things, you know. "Let me feel your head; let me feel your arm."

So I'm sitting in the emergency ward with my sore throat, and the doctor comes out and says, "What's the matter?"

"My son has a sore throat," my mother said.

The doctor says, "OK, we'll take a look at it. Say 'aah.'"

"Oh?" I said.

"Yes, well, this is it. Listen, he's really got it. He's got tonsillitis, Mrs. Cosby," said the doctor.

"Oh, well, what do you want to do?"

"Well, we do a tonsillectomy on Wednesday, which is the day after tomorrow. You can leave him here tonight."

"Who? You guys going to leave who? You're not leavin' me nowhere," I said.

"Well, you're just going to . . . we're going to operate on you Wednesday," said the doctor.

"Operate who? Ma, don't let them. Please don't let them do nothing bad. What are they going to cut?" I cried.

"Well, don't worry about it; just going to cut two things in your throat," explained the doctor.

"TWO THINGS IN MY THROAT! And then I won't be able to talk, or what?" I asked.

"Yes, you'll be able to talk. Listen, son, let me explain to you. Your tonsils, which we are going to have to take out, guard your throat, you see. They stand there. They're two guards. And anything bad that comes into your mouth, they fight it off. BSCHHH! See, well, in your case, your tonsils have lost the war. As a matter

of fact, they have gone as far as to join the other side, you see, and
they're going to kill you if we don't cut them out," said the doctor.

"Well, it's going to hurt and everything," I said.

"No, we're not going to hurt you. Now listen, as a matter of fact
— listen to me now — when they cut your tonsils out, don't you
know (Are you ready for the lie?), THEY'LL GIVE YOU ALL
THE ICE CREAM IN THE WORLD YOU CAN EAT!" the doctor
said.

"Is that right? I can have all the ice cream in the world I can
eat?" I asked.

"Yes, I'm not kidding," said the doctor.

"You won't tell me no fibs, now, Mom?" I asked.

"No, no. I'm not kidding. All the ice cream . . ." said my mom.

"Boy, you guys are in trouble, . . . 'cause I can eat a MESS of ice cream. I'm telling you now, I. . . . One time I ate a whole elephant full of chocolate ice cream. Can I have chocolate?"

"You can have chocolate," said the doctor.

"Oh, boy! Take me wherever I'm supposed to go now. You can cut off my whole neck for some chocolate ice cream, man," I said.

So they marched me in and I turned in my civvies, and they gave me that hospital thing that you put on where the back is open, and you're afraid — you know, you back away from people, and you bump into the walls, and they're, uh, marble walls, ice cold. And the iron cribs are ice cold. They're so cold you stick to the cribs, you know. Gee whiz, man!

So I marched on the ward. And they introduced me to my two buddies.

"This is Johnson."

"HEY, Johnson, how you doing? You going to get some ice cream, too?" I asked.

"Yes, they told me I'd get some ice cream, but . . ." said Johnson.

"Yes, well, listen, man. When the nurse leaves I'll talk to you about that ice cream later, 'cause we're going to eat a MESS of ice cream," I said.

"And this is Rudolph."

"How you doing, Rud? You going to get some ice cream?" I asked.

"Yes, yes, I'm getting some ice cream. Yes, oh boy! I eat it up," Rudolph said.

"OK, oh boy! . . . All right, nurse, you may leave now. We're all right," I said.

So I sat down. We looked at each other and we said:

"Ice Cream. ICE cream! We're going to eat ICE cream! And we'll eat it every day, in-the-middle-of-the-night. We're singing, ICE cream! We'll eat that ICE cream . . ."

Then I said, "Listen. You know what I'm going to do when I get my first bowl of ice cream? I'm not even going to touch it, or eat it, or nothing. I'm going to smear it all over my body, man. Just smear it all over my face and eyes and hair and everywhere. I'm going to be the most BEAUTIFUL SUNDAE YOU EVER SEEN IN YOUR LIFE! ICE cream! I'm going to eat ICE cream! I'm telling you now — ICE cream! Sing along with me now . . ."

And the whole day passed, man. Every time the orderly brought by the breakfast cart, man — F-F-F-T!

"All right. It's time for breakfast," he'd say, and we'd eat it up. Man, our stomachs would swell up we ate so much. You got to keep eating a lot so your stomach will stretch, man.

"Bring in the dinner! — R-R-R-R — and the supper! — R-R-R-R. Make it stretch out!" We ate everything, man, preparing for the ice cream. OK. And we didn't even sleep the night of surgery.

"Hey, man, yes, we're going to get some ice cream and everything. ICE cream! We're going to get ICE cream!" we yelled.

And that morning, the orderly went by with the breakfast cart — F-F-F-T!

"Hey! You, almost a doctor! Come here with that thing, man. We got to eat this morning," I called.

"You're not getting nothing to eat," he said.

"How come?" I asked.

"Because you're getting your tonsils out," he said.

"Well, what's that got to do with it?" I asked.

"When you get your tonsils out, you can't have any food in your stomach because you'll throw up," he said.

"Are you kidding? One time I ate a dead frog; I didn't throw up or nothin', man! Bring that breakfast cart back here."

And he went away — F-F-F-T! In came the nurse with the gurney. You know the gurney's the thing that they put you on to take you down to surgery. And the wheels on the gurneys are always the same. They always have that wobble like there is a windstorm going on about six inches above the ground — WHALooDLELooDLELooDLELooDLE!

So she wheeled it in; we all sit up. "ICE cream! We're going to eat ICE cream!" we screamed.

"All right, now, it's time to go to surgery. Who's going first?" she asked.

"Take me!" I said.

"No, take me! I want to go!" said Johnson.

"No, no, listen. C before V and S. You guys get strawberry and vanilla, and I'm C, and alphabetically I go first, you know," I said.

"No, we're going to take Johnson because he was here first," said the nurse.

"Oh, shucks. . . . OK, Jonse! Go ahead, man. Get that ice cream! Cut it up there! All right, go ahead, Jonse!"

Johnson stepped on the gurney. "Well, I guess you know what this means. If they run out of strawberry, vanilla and chocolate are in jeopardy!" he said.

"Okay, Jonse! Don't eat it up from us, though! Heyyy, Johnson. Johnson, go ahead, babe!"

And we sat down and we looked at each other.

"ICE cream! We're going to eat ICE cream!" And, BOOM!

"Johnson's back! OK, are you ready? Yes, me too. Go ahead, Jonse. Heyyy, Jonse! . . . Wake up!

"Hey, Johnson, how come your eyeballs just keep waving around in the air? That's catsup, right? That's catsup on his mouth, coming down from his mouth? Isn't it catsup? Please say it's catsup, because we hate to think that you KILLED JOHNSON! . . . THEY KILLED JOHNSON!"

They picked him up. Johnson was like a wet rag — oBoLaBoLaBoLaBoLa!

"Oh, man!" said Rudolph.

"All right, who's next?"

"Get away from me! Fight them off, Rudy! I'll head them off here. They aren't touching neither one of us!" I screamed.

Rudy started crying — "A-A-A-A-I-I-I!" (Rudy had the funniest cry you ever wanted to see. He would run whenever he cried — ohWAlaWAlaWAlaWAla!) And they picked him up and they strapped him down on the gurney, man, and they took him away.

"Rudy, keep fighting, babe! Keep fighting! Just remember one thing: keep your mouth closed! Johnson, Johnson, wake up, babe. ICE cream! You got to sing with me, ICE cream! Oh, he's dead," I said.

BOOM!

"All right, Rudy, did you keep your? . . . No, you didn't keep it . . . they got him," I said.

"OK, William. You're next."

"Oh, wait, wait. Before you touch me, I have a confession to make. Does it mean anything to you if I say I just had breakfast? OK, I'll go peacefully," I said.

And they put me on a gurney, and they covered me up with a sheet up to my neck, and put me on the elevator. And I knew I was going to die. And I really hadn't prepared myself for it. And it was pitiful. You know, when you're only five years old and your life passes before you, it's pitiful, man. You really don't have that much of a life to pass before you. It was just a little F-F-F-F-T — and then it was gone. I had to call for a rerun.

And they brought me into surgery; doctors and nurses all got their masks on so you can't tell who they are. And they put the needle in my arm and let the thing go. And the doctor says, "Count backward from one hundred."

"One hundred, ninety — " I didn't even make it to the second nine, I was so pitiful.

And . . . the thing pressed me t-h-r-o-u-g-h the t-a-b-l-e, and I remember that I wanted to wake up.

I said to myself, "Wake up, wake up, wake up."

"Yep, it's time to wake up," I answered.

"Well, why don't you open your eyes?"

"No. Don't want to."

"How come?"

"Well, because every time I open my eyes, the room starts to act silly, going around in circles and jumping up and down. I don't want to wake up. I'll just stay like this — half awake, half asleep — and just hummmmmmmmmm a little bit."

"How's your mouth feel?"

"Oh, it's dry, very dry."

"And your tongue?"

"It's dry too, yes. And the lips are dry and the tongue is dry and the mouth is dry and the throat is dry, and everything is dry, dry, dry, dry, dry."

"Well, do you want to swallow?"

"Yes."

"Well, why don't you?"

"Nobody asked me."

"All right, try to give me a little swallow."

"OK." BSCHHHH!! "Ummmmmmmm."

"Hello, brain?"

"Yes."

"This is throat."

"Yes."

"You better get some work done down here. Somebody killed the kid or something."

"Hello? Hello, kid?"

"Hummm?"

"You want to try to swallow?"

"Huh-uh."

"Try and swallow again. We want to check out the trouble."

"No."

"Try. Come on now."

BSCHHHH!!!!! . . . "Ice cream . . ."

Hand in Hand

The Muffin Muncher

Stephen Cosgrove

When there are problems, often they can be solved by people
working together. The king and villagers of a very poor castle have
a problem: A monstrous muffin-munching dragon. A solution is
needed. As you read this story, you will see how working hand in
hand can be exactly what is needed to solve problems for kings and
dragons as well as for people.

Many, many years ago in the far corner of a very poor country stood the poorest of poor castles.

The villagers of the castle did not have riches and valuables. They were also poor in spirit. They had done nothing to be proud of.

The only way they had stayed alive at all was by baking and selling the best muffins in the land.

Every morning the king, who was also the head baker, would bake a fresh batch. When he had finished, the people would load their carts and set off for the other villages in the kingdom.

There was never any trouble selling the muffins. They were the finest ever baked. But because the people were so poor, they had to use all the money they had earned to buy wood for the fire and flour to make more.

So, day in and day out, the head baker, who was also the king, would build up the giant fires in the ovens and bake muffins.

He would slowly mix all the ingredients in a big cracked bowl. Then he would pour the mix into the tins, and put them in the ovens to bake.

The people were just barely getting along. As if things were not bad enough, there appeared at the castle one day a great dragon. Now, this was not your everyday, run-of-the-mill dragon. He was rather large. He was a little heavy. He was a muffin-munching dragon.

With crumbs still on his face from the last muffins he'd eaten, he came down the hill, right up to the bridge.

Taking one look, the people ran over the bridge and into the castle.

The dragon took a great long smell. He said, "I smell muffins!" This castle, he decided, smelled like a nice place to stay. He moved in, right under the bridge.

He was very tired from his long journey. So he took his pillow and the picture of his pony from his bag, curled up, and fell fast asleep.

The next morning the people looked out their castle windows and thought that the dragon was gone. Breathing a sigh, they began preparing for another day.

After loading their wagons with fresh warm muffins, they set off across the bridge, over the soundly sleeping dragon. With all the noise from the wagons, he woke up.

He peeked over the edge to see what was going on. "So, that's it. Those muffins look so good and I am very hungry."

He thought and thought and finally came up with a plan. He jumped up on the bridge right in front of the people, tried to look

very mean, and roared. "Stop, or I shall burn up your bridge!" Then he blew a little flame and puffed three smoke rings.

"From now on," he rumbled, "you shall each give me ten of your best muffins as your price to cross my bridge."

"But this is our bridge!" they cried.

"Well, if I burn it up, it won't be anybody's bridge," said the dragon.

The people thought and talked awhile and finally agreed to give the dragon what he wanted. They barely had enough money to buy wood, let alone enough wood to build a new bridge.

From then on, every wagon that crossed the bridge left ten muffins. With crumbs all around him, he would sit there, stuffing those scrumptious muffins away.

This might have gone on to this day except for one little thing. The dragon was eating so many muffins that the people did not have enough to sell. Because of that, they didn't have enough money to buy wood for the ovens or even flour to bake more.

They would return every day with fewer goods. One day they all came home with nothing.

The next morning the head baker, who was also the king, could not fire up the great ovens because there was no wood. He could not use his big cracked bowl because he had no flour or goods to put in it.

With a heavy heart and a tear in his eye, the baker sat sadly on a pile of empty flour sacks and cried. "We have no more goods to make muffins. We have no more wood to light the fires. We cannot bake any more muffins. Our bridge will be burned down. What are we ever to do?"

That same day the dragon woke up, brushed his teeth, combed his hair, and prepared for another day of munching.

He waited and waited and waited. No wagons came. His stomach began to rumble and roar. He tried eating a few of the crumbs that had dropped on the ground the day before. They were stale. "No muffins?" he roared.

Finally he decided to enter the castle and find out what had happened to all his muffins.

The dragon walked through the castle until he reached the bakery. Then he peeked inside. "Where are my muffins?" he roared. "I've been waiting and waiting and waiting! Where are they?"

The head baker, who was also the king, walked up to the dragon as bravely as he could. "Mr. Dragon," he said, "we are poor people. We live in a poor castle which has very little. Before you came, the muffins we sold barely paid for our wood and goods to mix. Now that we have to give you so many muffins, we can't buy enough wood. Our ovens have no heat."

That poor dragon was so very confused. He wanted some muffins because he was so hungry. But at the same time he felt sorry for the baker and the other people who lived in the castle.

He thought and thought. Finally, a great big smile crossed his face. "I have it!" he shouted. He asked the head baker, who was also the king, to call all the people to a castle meeting so that he could tell them of his wonderful plan.

The people happily began to cheer and shout as he finished. Surely the dragon had solved the castle's problems, and his own.

Then and for always, the dragon heated the ovens of the bakery with his mighty flame. With the extra money they saved by not having to buy wood, the people were able to leave a stack of muffins in reach of the muffin-munching dragon.

While heating up the ovens
With a lot of style and grace,
The muffin muncher smiles a smile
With crumbs upon his face.

The Southpaw

Judith Viorst

Everyone needs friends, but sometimes making friends can be a little difficult. Read "The Southpaw" to find out how Janet and Richard become friends.

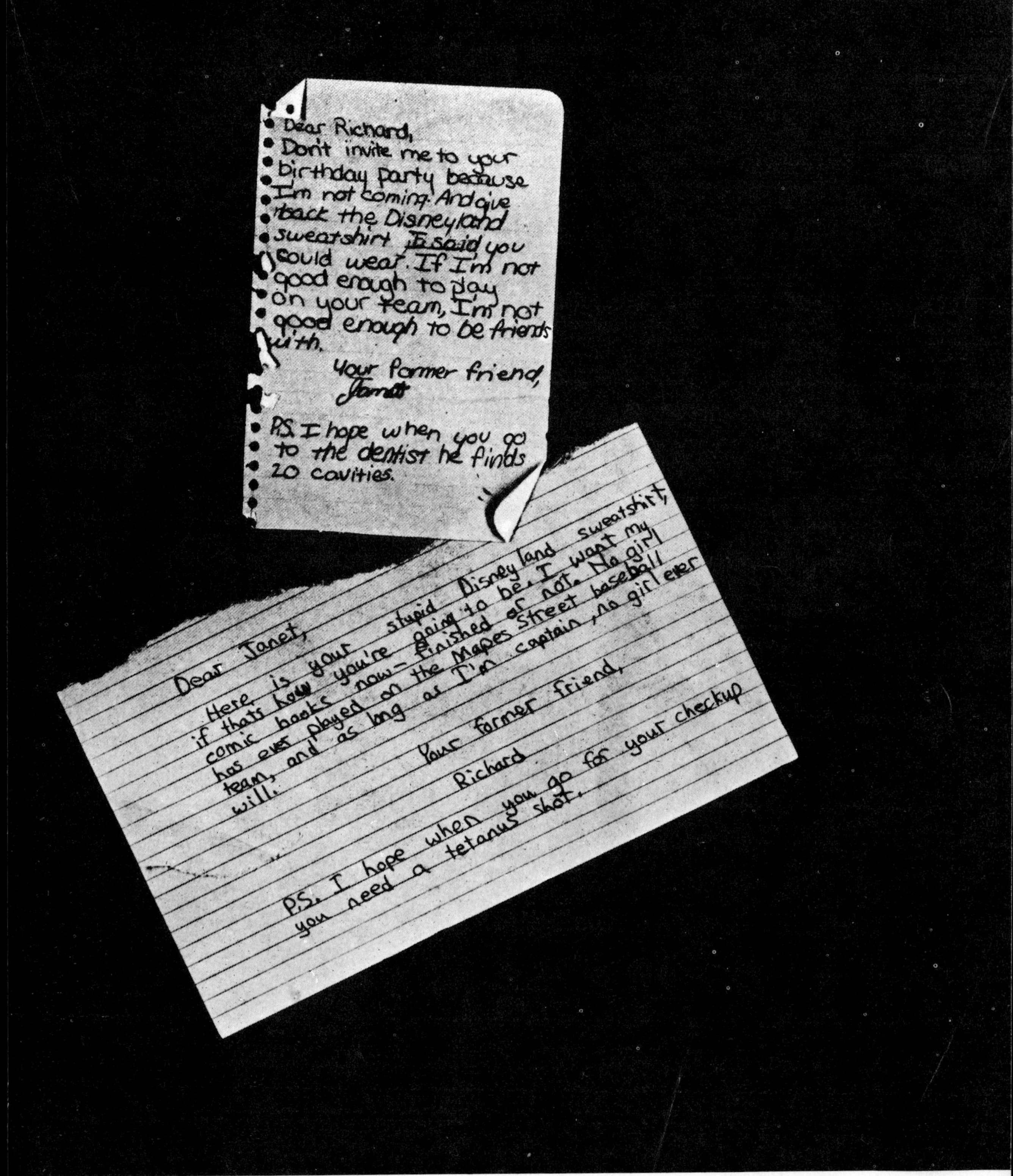

Dear Richard,
Don't invite me to your birthday party because I'm not coming. And give back the Disneyland sweatshirt I said you could wear. If I'm not good enough to play on your team, I'm not good enough to be friends with.

Your former friend,
Janet

P.S. I hope when you go to the dentist he finds 20 cavities.

Dear Janet,
Here is your stupid Disneyland sweatshirt, if thats how you're going to be. I want my comic books now — finished Street baseball has ever played on the Mapes team, and as long as I'm captain, no girl ever will.

Your former friend,
Richard

P.S. I hope when you go for your checkup you need a tetanus shot.

Dear Richard,
I'm changing my goldfish's name from Richard to Stanley. Don't count on my vote for class president next year. Just because I'm a member of the ballet club doesn't mean I'm not a terrific ballplayer.
Your former friend,
Janet

P.S. I see you lost your first game 28-0

Dear Janet,
I'm not saving anymore seats for you on the bus. For all I care you can stand the whole way to school. Why don't you just forget about baseball and learn something nice like knitting.
Your former friend,

Richard

P.S. Wait until Wednesday.

Dear Richard,
My father said I could call someone to go with us for a ride and hot-fudge sundaes. In case you didn't notice, I didn't call you.

Your former friend,
Janet

P.S. I see you lost your second game, 34-0.

Dear Janet,
Remember I took the laces out of my blue-and-white sneakers and gave them to you? I want them back.
Your former friend,
Richard

P.S. Wait until Friday.

Dear Richard,
Congratulations on your unbroken record. Eight straight losses, wow! I understand you're the laughingstock of New Jersey.
Your former-friend,
Janet

P.S. Why don't you and your team forget about baseball and learn something nice like knitting maybe?

Dear Janet,
Here's the silver horseback riding trophy that you gave me. I don't think I want to keep it anymore.
Your former friend,
Richard
P.S. I didn't think you'd be the kind who'd kick a man when he's down.

Dear Richard,
I wasn't kicking exactly, I was kicking back.
Your former friend,
Janet
P.S. In case you were wondering, my batting average is .345.

Dear Janet,
Alfie is having his tonsils out tomorrow. We might be able to let you catch next week.
Richard

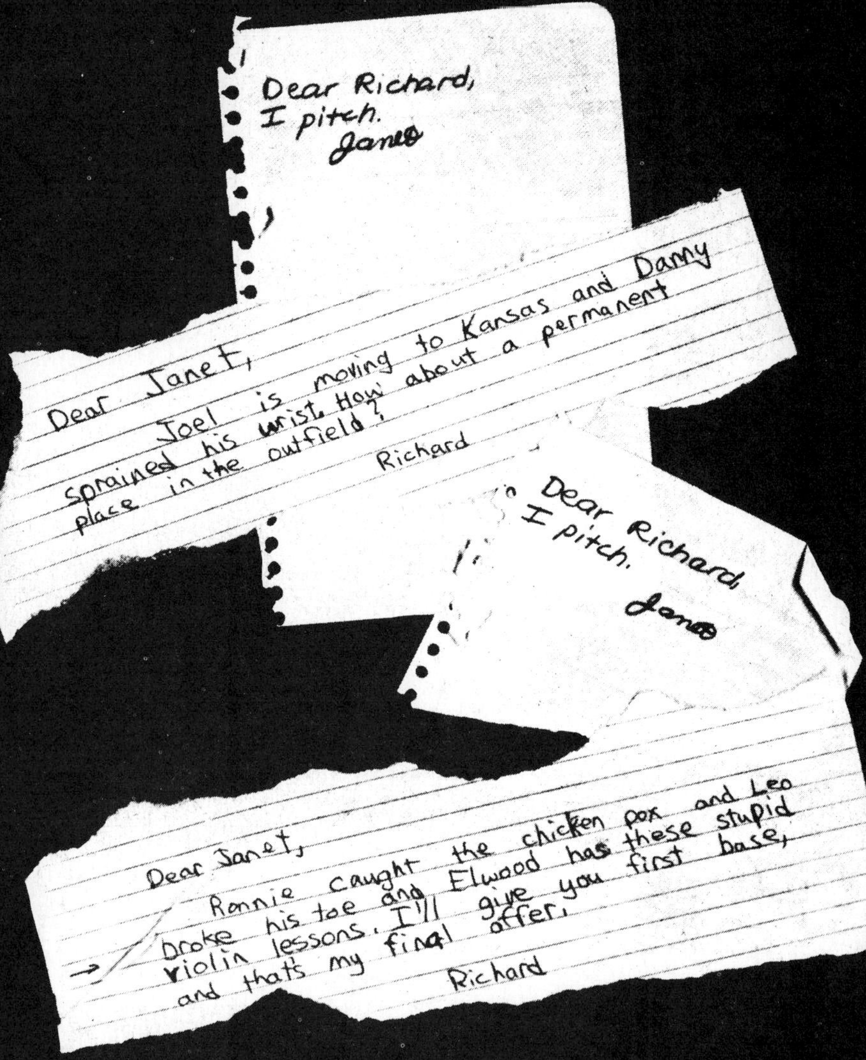

Dear Richard,
I pitch.
Janet

Dear Janet,
   Joel is moving to Kansas and Danny sprained his wrist. How about a permanent place in the outfield?
              Richard

Dear Richard,
I pitch.
Janet

Dear Janet,
   Ronnie caught the chicken pox and Leo broke his toe and Elwood has these stupid violin lessons. I'll give you first base, and that's my final offer.
              Richard

Dear Richard,
Susan Reilly plays
first base, Marilyn Jackson
catches, Ethel Kahn
plays center field, I
pitch. It's a package
deal.
        Janet
P.S. Sorry about your
12-game losing streak.

Dear Janet,
    Please! Not Marilyn Jackson.
                Richard

Dear Richard,
Nobody ever said that I
was unreasonable. How
about Lizzie Martindale
instead?
        Janet

Dear Janet,
    At least could you call your goldfish Richard
again?
            your friend
            Richard

The Treasure of Sumiko's Bay

Barbara Chamberlain

All over the world, people need to work to earn a living. This story tells about Sumiko's very different kind of work. Sumiko and her grandmother raise oysters for the pearls. When Sumiko discovers that thieves are stealing the oysters, she must be clever as well as brave. How can Sumiko save the oysters that she and her grandmother need?

Sumiko found the broken threads on her first dive into the warm water of the bay. For the last two months, the girl had found that small clumps of valuable oysters were missing from their

home on the rocky floor of the inlet. Yesterday she tied sewing thread across each of the bamboo poles that marked the oyster beds.

Sumiko surfaced for air and hung to the raft between the poles. "They came last night!" The girl knew every shell in the beds. She checked them in their watery home every day to keep them safe from such animals as hungry starfish. "It couldn't be anyone from my village," she told herself. "A thief must come in from the ocean, through the small opening in the mountains."

There was no other way to enter the bay, ringed on all sides by high mountains, the highest on the island of Okinawa. The mountains sat directly in the water, except for one small beach below Sumiko's northern village.

The twelve-year-old girl swam to shore. She did not stop at the beach to say hello to the village women washing their clothes in the stream which flowed down from the rice terraces. She ran directly to the home of the mayor of their small village. His house, with its gray roof, stood out among the sixteen other straw-roofed houses.

"A broken thread is not enough, Sumiko," Mayor Yamada told her. "A large fish may have done it, and taken the oysters as well. A strong pull from the tide could also have broken the threads."

He didn't understand. She knew every oyster growing in the beds, and some were missing. "If I were older," Sumiko thought, "or if Father were alive, the mayor would pay more attention." *It was up to her to do something, but what?*

At Sumiko's one-room home, her grandmother served a meal of sweet potatoes mixed with rice. The sweet flavor tasted good for a change from their usual meal of rice and cabbage.

"The oysters are ours, Grandmother. I work hard to keep them safe. I can't let someone steal our years of work."

Her grandmother poured tea. "You're not imagining the loss?"

"No! I've been diving and caring for the beds since I was small."

"You learned everything so well when you were small. Your father taught you carefully when he found he had the same sickness that took your mother." Grandmother opened her sleeping mat. "If you are right, they must come in by boat from one of the villages on the China Sea. But what can an old woman and a twelve-year-old girl do?"

"Grandmother, the oysters are our living. Everyone else farms the rice terraces, but we have no land. We must keep them safe until we sell the pearls and the shells."

Two weeks later, Sumiko slipped leather covers over her hands for protection and dived into the warm water. Since it took seven years for the pearls to become large enough to sell, each bed held oysters planted in a different year. "By now the robbers know which are the large pearl beds," she thought.

A white spot stood out on the waving moss that stuck to the gray oysters. Reaching into the bed, she found three white shellfish eating three of the oysters. She surfaced for breath and put the shellfish in a bag that hung around her neck. These shells were a danger.

The oysters rested on their left sides on the inlet floor and would never leave that spot. They were easy for any hungry fish to eat. The spiral shell snail drilled through the oyster shell and sucked out the meat. Even if allowed to destroy only a few, soon

they would multiply. If left alone, they would destroy the beds.

Sumiko dived again and again that morning, looking at the beds carefully. She gathered a dozen drill shells, more than she had seen in a year.

She and her grandmother could sell the shells to a shopkeeper on their monthly walk to a large village down the coast, where they also sold pearls.

The girl swam to shore. Wringing out her white top and black cotton skirt, she sat on the beach to dry off.

She lifted a drill shell from her bag. The animal shut its aperture tightly. Sumiko held it in her hand, knowing the animal would soon die. "I'm sorry. You don't have an evil plan. You take only for your own food, but I must protect the oysters. Whoever is stealing our oysters is certainly throwing away the animals and selling the pearls. I must catch them! If only they couldn't get into the bay . . ."

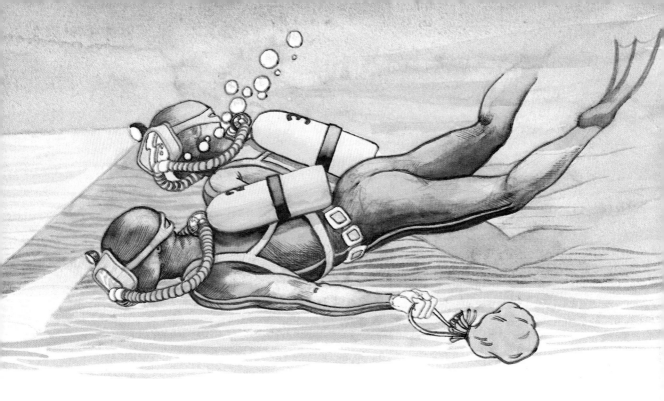

There was a chance to do something! She raced home to tell her plan to Grandmother.

After their plans were finished, Sumiko and her grandmother spent five nights on the beach, sleeping when they could. During the day Sumiko tried ways of slipping quietly through the water, not making a splash or sound. Knowing that she could swim better than anyone in the village lessened her fears of being caught when the robbers *did* come.

"I may have to give up tomorrow, Sumiko. My old bones like to sleep in our home," her grandmother said. "And now that the moon has left, we can't see very well."

Sumiko had been sleeping for only a short time when a sound from the bay woke her. She heard splashing from the direction of the oyster rafts. "Of course! They waited for a dark night!" She whispered to her grandmother to awaken the people of the village. Then Sumiko slipped silently into the water.

Her feet kicked strongly, and she used her arms underwater, with her nose barely out of the water.

Yes, she could see the shadows of two men by a canoe. Her heart seemed to pound through the water, so loud she thought the men would hear. But they were too busy diving with some kind of lights they wore attached to their face masks.

Closing the new gate to the bay was the first part of her plan. She and her grandmother had lashed some of the bamboo poles together during their week of waiting. They tied them to the rocks on one side of the ocean opening, where they could not be seen at night. Sumiko swung them around. She tied them tightly to the rocks above and under the water. Then she swam straight for the canoe.

Splash! One of the men surfaced by the boat. Sumiko slipped under the water. When the man dived again, Sumiko swiftly cut the canoe's anchor rope and raced to shore with the boat.

Grandmother put her arm around the girl's shaking shoulders. "The two men are trapped in the bay. They can't swim forever."

Finally the robbers swam to the small shore where the village people waited with lanterns. They tried to run, but the people gathered around them. There was no escape.

"We will take you to the island police in the morning," Mayor Yamada said. "Nothing like this has ever happened in our village, and we want to be certain it won't happen again. To think a young girl showed the rest of us how to catch these men."

"You mean that girl trapped us?" one of the men grumbled.

"Sumiko and her grandmother. We have the evidence against you in the boat." The mayor turned to Sumiko and said, "I'm sorry you have lost more of your oysters."

"The ones in the boat are dead, but we can sell the pearls," Grandmother told him.

Sumiko took one of the oysters from the boat and opened it with her knife. She felt for the hard, round lump, and even in the dark night the white gleam from the oyster flashed between her fingers as she lifted it from the shell.

"You have saved our treasure, Sumiko." Grandmother smiled. "Now let's go home. These old bones have had enough excitement to last for a long time!"

A Twister of Twists, A Tangler of Tongues____

Alvin Schwartz

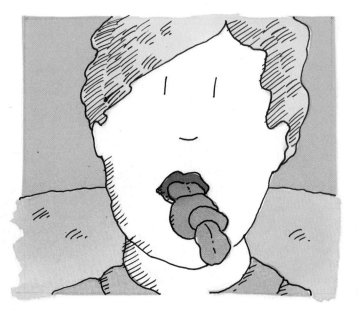

   Happiness is needed all over the world. Tongue twisters have brought smiles and laughter to many people. Here are some English, German, Spanish, and Italian tongue twisters to tickle your tongue and twist your tonsils.

I need not your needles
　　They're needless to me,
For needing needles
　　Is needless, you see,
But did my neat trousers
　　But need to be kneed,
I then should have need
　　Of your needles indeed.

Theophilus Thistledown,
   the successful thistle sifter,
in sifting a sieve of unsifted thistles,
   thrust three thousand thistles
through the thick of his thumb.
   If, then, Theophilus Thistledown,
the successful thistle sifter,
   thrust three thousand thistles
through the thick of his thumb,
   see that thou,
in sifting a sieve of thistles,
   do not get the unsifted thistles
stuck in *thy* thumb.

Mr. See owned a saw
 And Mr. Soar owned a seesaw.
Now See's saw sawed Soar's seesaw
 Before Soar saw See
Which made Soar sore.
 Had Soar seen See's saw
Before See sawed Soar's seesaw,
 See's saw would not have sawed
Soar's seesaw.
 So See's saw sawed Soar's seesaw.
But it was a shame to see Soar so sore
 Just because See's saw sawed
Soar's seesaw.

GERMAN

Fischers Fritz fischt frische Fische.
Frische Fische fischt Fischers Fritz.

Fishers Fritz fisht *frish*-eh *fish*-eh.
Frish-eh *fish*-eh fisht Fischers Fritz.

Fritz Fischer fishes for fresh fish.
Fresh fish fish for Fritz Fischer.

SPANISH

Yo no compro coco. Porque como poco coco,
poco coco compro.

Yo no *kom*-pro *ko*ko. Por-*kay ko*mo *po*ko *ko*ko,
*po*ko *ko*ko *kom*-pro.

I do not buy coconut. Since I eat little coconut,
I buy little coconut.

Mi mamá me mima mucho.

Me ma*ma* me *mee*-ma *moo*-cho.

My mother spoils me a lot.

ITALIAN

Paolo, pittore poco pratico, pinse pillole per
poco prezzo.

Paw-lo, pit-*to*-rey *po*ko *pra*-tico, *pin*-sey *pil*-lo-
ley per *po*ko *pret*-zo.

Paul, an inexperienced painter, painted pills
cheaply.

Un limon, mezzo limon.

Oon lee-*mon*, medzo lee-*mon*.

One lemon, half a lemon.

Animal Tools

George F. Mason

*Fur and feathers, teeth and claws
—animals seem remarkably fitted for
their lives. But they need more than
weapons. Read this article to find out
more about animals and their needs.*

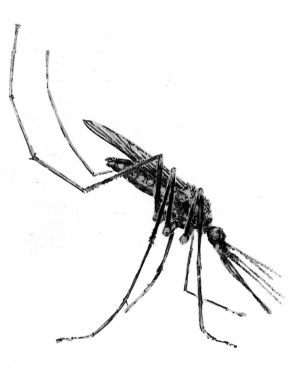

When was the last time you did some work? What kind did you do? Did you use tools? Maybe you did. People often use tools. Sometimes they use their hands as tools. But most of the time they hold the tools with their hands and do the work with the tools.

Most animals use parts of their bodies as tools. Probably the most important tools animals have are their teeth.

Animal teeth are used for cutting and grinding food, but they may be used for other reasons, too. Animals such as foxes have long, sharp eyeteeth, which they use in killing or fighting. Beavers have long front teeth, which they can use to cut down trees. Rabbits and many other animals also have long front teeth. They are used to bite off bark and twigs.

The animals that eat grass have another kind of teeth. Their teeth are wide and flat and are used for grinding food. Cows and deer have teeth of this kind.

The largest teeth that we know of are the tusks of the elephants. The elephants use their tusks in digging for food and in fighting.

One strange set of animal tools is that used by a mosquito for getting food. A mosquito doesn't really bite, as many people think it does. It can't bite, for it has no teeth.

If you watch a mosquito, you will see that it seems to push its bill into

the skin, but this isn't what really happens. The mosquito's bill is only its lower lip. But inside the lip is a set of tiny tools. There are a pair of saws, a pair of tubes, and some tiny knives in this set of tools. The mosquito uses all of them when it gets food.

When a mosquito is hungry, it looks for a soft spot in an animal's skin. After finding this spot, it puts its bill on the skin and begins to cut. The tiny saws and knives in the set of tools quickly cut through the skin. Then the two tubes in the bill are pushed in. One puts saliva into the blood to keep it thin. The other sucks up blood.

Only the female mosquito has this strange set of tools, for the male does not live on blood. It lives on plant juices instead. But the hungry female will suck blood until her body is red.

Another strange set of tools is the bittern's cleaning tools. This bird has powder puffs, fine powder, combs, and feather oil. On each leg the bittern has some soft, fluffy feathers that hold the fine powder. Under the middle toe on each foot there is a comb. And on the top part of the tail there is a place where the feather oil comes out.

The bittern often feeds on fish or eels. When it catches and eats these animals, it gets slime on its feathers. The bird spends one to two hours cleaning up after each feeding.

First it puts the fine powder on its feathers. The powder makes the feathers look as though they had been dusted with flour. The bird lets this dry on its feathers. Then it uses its combs to loosen the dried slime. After much shaking of the feathers, all the powder and the loose slime are gone. Next the bittern gets oil with its bill from its tail. The bird puts this oil over its feathers. Soon the bird is clean, and the feathers are shiny again.

Bitterns aren't the only animals that have combs. Beavers and a few other animals have combs, too. Beavers have a comb that is part of the nail on the second toe of each back foot.

Since they are very clean animals, they spend a lot of time combing their thick fur and keeping it clean and soft.

Think About This:

1. What do animals use their teeth for?
2. What does a mosquito do when it is hungry?
3. How does the bittern clean its body?
4. Can you think of some more animal tools?

People all over the world need food to eat, clothes to wear, and a place to live. But people have other very special needs. The following poems describe needs that are important to everyone.

Dreams to Sell

If there were dreams to sell,
    What would you buy?
Some cost a passing bell;
    Some a light sigh,
That shakes from Life's fresh crown
Only a rose-leaf down.
If there were dreams to sell,
Merry and sad to tell,
And the crier rang the bell,
What would you buy?

T. L. Beddoes

The Question

If I could teach you how to fly
Or bake an elderberry pie
Or turn the sidewalk into stars
Or play new songs on an old guitar
Or if I knew the way to heaven,
The names of night, the taste of seven
And owned them all, to keep or lend —
Would you come and be my friend?

You cannot teach me how to fly.
I love the berries but not the pie.
The sidewalks are for walking on,
And an old guitar has just one song.
The names of night cannot be known,
The way to heaven cannot be shown.
You cannot keep, you cannot lend —
But still I want you for my friend.

Dennis Lee

To Look at Any Thing

To look at any thing,
If you would know that thing,
You must look at it long:
To look at this green and say,
'I have seen spring in these
Woods,' will not do — you must
Be the thing you see:
You must be the dark snakes of
Stems and ferny plumes of leaves,
You must enter in
To the small silences between
The leaves,
You must take your time
And touch the very peace
They issue from.

John Moffitt

Pitcher

Stephen Cole

The new boy has a punched-in nose and ears that stick out, so Monk nicknames him Pitcher. From that moment Pitcher is someone for the other boys, especially Monk, to pick on. Everyone needs friends. Pitcher's only real friend is his roommate, who tells this story. Read to find out how Pitcher finds an answer to his need for friends.

I was late finishing my test, and when I hurried out into the hall, there stood Monk grabbing Pitch by the collar. He was holding him there in his left hand while he waved his right fist under Pitcher's nose. There was murder in Monk's eye, so I hurried over.

"When I want to look on your paper, you let me look!" I heard him hiss at Pitcher. He shook Pitch until his teeth rattled, and for a second I thought he was going to paste him.

"What's the matter?" I asked, butting in.

"I wanted to look on Pitcher's paper during that test, that's all!" Monk shouted at me. "The little rat wouldn't let me. He turned the paper around."

"He's left-handed," I tried to explain. "You just write left-handed on one of those desks and see if you don't turn the paper around, too."

Monk looked startled. He dropped his balled-up fist and took his hand off Pitcher's collar. Then he flared up again. "I bet he'd have turned it around if he was right-handed!"

"Maybe I would have, at that," said Pitcher. He stood there, the skinny little owl, just looking at Monk. Sometimes it seems to me that Pitch hasn't any sense at all. Nobody but an idiot would try to egg Monk on, particularly if that idiot is as puny as Pitcher. I bet Monk weighs a good ten pounds more than Pitch.

Monk whipped his arm back, and I was just going to grab his fist when Mr. Harper came around the corner at the end of the hall. He took one quick look at us, and I don't know about the other guys, but my heart stopped beating. But Mr. Harper didn't say much.

"Why aren't you boys in your classroom?" was all he said. It was enough. We beat it. We practically tumbled into Mr. Andrews' Latin class. Mr. Harper is a pretty good guy for a headmaster, but you don't fool around with him. You don't fool around any.

I didn't get a chance to talk to Pitcher again that day until we were in our room after lunch. But you can bet I went to work on him then, especially when he gave me a good opportunity by picking up a book as if he was going to study, even when he didn't have to.

"You study more than most of us, don't you, Pitch?" I said. I wanted to lead up to the subject that was on my mind, and this seemed a good way.

"I hope I'm not just a grind," he said, grinning at me. Pitcher has a nice grin.

"Oh no, you're not a grind," I told him in a hurry. "But most of us don't hardly study at all."

"My mother asked me to try to make good grades," he said. He looked embarrassed, and I don't blame him. If he'd made a remark like that out in public, the whole gang would have busted out laughing in his face. At a boarding school it is practically indecent to mention your mother in a tone of voice like that.

"Oh," was all I could say. I looked somewhere else.

"She doesn't have too much money," he said. He was staring straight out the window, so it was safe now to turn back and look at him. "She asked me please to get all I could out of this school. And to put as much into it as possible. She said she always wanted to be proud of me."

"Oh," I said again.

"So I'm doing the best I can," Pitch went on. His face was very red, and his eyes were blinking fast behind his glasses. I guess he felt he had to say what he was saying, but of course he wanted to get it over with as fast as he could. "You see, I like my mother," he said.

This time I didn't even say "Oh." I had never heard anything like that before in my life. It took me a couple of seconds, thinking my fastest, to dig up another subject. Then I lighted on the thing that was really on my mind.

"But you can't let Monk push you around!" I said. "You can't keep your nose so close to the paper that you forget Monk and make him get mad at you!"

"Why can't I?" Pitch asked. "Why can't I when he's trying to cheat?"

Now I'm not the smartest guy in the world, but I saw right away that there was no use in trying to argue that point with Pitch, especially when I had a sneaking idea he was right. So I started prowling up and down the room, trying to find a new idea. An idea that would save Pitch from being murdered, because it was perfectly clear that he was right smack in the middle. It was all right with me if he wanted to study hard to please his mother — just so long as he didn't talk about a thing like that out in public — but at the same time he couldn't let Monk push him around. And those two facts didn't seem to mix well.

Then the idea came. I stopped prowling around and slammed my hand down on Pitcher's shoulder. He winced. "Tell you what we'll do!" I shouted. "We'll gang up on Monk! You and I'll stick together and not take any guff off Monk."

For a moment I thought about how noble that idea was, and then a couple of other thoughts began to crowd my head. The first was that Pitch wasn't about to take any of Monk's guff, as it was. And two against one wasn't so good either, so I put the other thought into loud words. "Only then he'll get you alone someday and beat you to a bloody pulp."

"Maybe not," said Pitch. "I can box."

I went around from where I was standing, stooped down with my hands on the table, and looked him in the eye.

"Wait a second, Pitch," I said. "You better come again with that. What did you say?"

"I said I can box."

I straightened up and drew in a breath, thinking of the terrible athlete Pitcher had been on the football field. There was a chair behind me, so I sat down. "All right, Pitcher," I said when I was sitting steady. "You can let me have it now. Who taught you how to box?"

"My father," he said. He said it quietly, looking out the window again.

"Your father. . . ."

"Yes," he said. He smiled, and his eyes weren't vacant anymore. "He was a pretty good boxer — he was champion of his college — and so he taught me how to box. He said I was the kind of a kid who would need to know how to box."

I nodded, thinking that Pitcher's father must be a pretty smart guy. All of a sudden I laughed out loud. "Then why in the world didn't you pole Monk up there in the hall between classes?" I jumped up, excited at the thought of the look on Monk's face if that had happened. "Why didn't you pole him?"

"Heck, I can't pole anybody," Pitcher said. "I'm not built right. All I can do is box. You know, the old straight left, only with me it's the right. It keeps them from hitting me, and maybe I jab a little blood out of their noses." He shrugged his shoulders. "Besides, I don't think my father would want me to do a thing like trying to pole Monk."

"Huh?" I said.

"I don't believe my father would think it was right." He wrinkled up his forehead, thinking hard. "You can't hit the other guy first when you're right," he said after a while. "You can't hit him when he doesn't expect it. Besides, you can't fight in the school building." He threw out his hands, kind of triumphant. "You see? I'm sure that's what my father would think."

I managed to say, "I'd like to meet your father someday."

"My father's dead," said Pitcher.

I got the creeps when he said that.

"He was a test pilot, and one day his jet disintegrated," I heard

him say. "Otherwise he'd have been an astronaut, sure. Remember a minute ago when you asked me why I didn't pole Monk? Remember that I stopped to think? Well, my father would have wanted me to think. See?"

I got up slowly. "Look, Pitch," I said. "I'm going outside. I think I'll go down to the ball field and run around the track or something. I think I need exercise."

"I'll go with you," said Pitcher.

We were in front of the school building, heading for the athletic field, when we came across Monk. Or rather, he came across us. He came slowly up to us, walking stiff-legged with his head down, and I noticed his eyes were narrow. He walked right up to Pitcher until their heads weren't more than six inches apart.

"I've been looking for you," Monk said. He talked through his teeth, the way they do on television when they're sore. So I gathered that Monk hadn't seen Pitch since first period in the morning.

"Yes?" said Pitch. He looked pale, but he didn't back up.

"I didn't like that crack you made," Monk said.

"No?" said Pitcher.

"That crack about maybe you'd turn your paper around even if you were right-handed."

"I think I probably would, you know," said Pitcher. "Cheating isn't —"

It was when he said that word that Monk poled him. Glasses and everything, Monk hauled off and poled him. Only Pitch turned his shoulder or something, and Monk missed him. He missed him so completely that he fell right into him, and Pitcher had to hold him up. Then Monk shoved hard and Pitch was sitting down on the ground.

Then, somehow or other, I found myself fighting Monk. Monk and I were squared off in the middle of a ring of guys — I don't know where they came from, but there they were in a ring around us — and we were throwing fists at each other. But not for long. It seemed like forever, but I guess it really wasn't a long time before I stepped on a rock, tripped, and fell flat on the ground. I was still on one knee, looking at my hands where I'd cut them on the gravel, when Monk kicked me. It didn't hurt much, but still he kicked me.

Before I could jump to my feet, some big guy in the crowd stuck out his hand to collar Monk, but he never did collar him. All he got in his hand was a pair of tortoiseshell glasses. Pitch had stuck his glasses into the hand, and before I can tell it, he was squared off fighting Monk.

Down there on the ground I looked up with my mouth hanging open, and I got the shock of my life. Because right over our heads, way up on the second floor of the school building, Mr. Harper was

leaning out to watch the fight. And he saw me. We looked right straight at each other. There wasn't a chance in the world to crawl away through all those legs, because we looked straight into each other's eyes.

Then Mr. Harper did a queer thing. He put his finger to his lips and shook his head slowly from side to side. With my mouth open I stared at him so long that finally he frowned and shook his head harder, his finger still on his lips. Then I caught on to the fact that he didn't want me to let on he was there. I stopped staring at him and got up to watch the fight myself. It all happened in a few seconds.

Pitcher was standing in the middle of the ring of guys, his long right arm stretched out, his chin tucked down behind his shoulder, and his left fist close to his chest. He was circling slowly all the time. It was fun to watch his feet because they never got tangled the way you'd think they would, knowing Pitch, and every now and then his hand would stab out. Not much. Just a couple of inches. Just a couple of inches straight ahead, with his shoulder behind it. And then he'd dance away.

When I could stop looking at Pitch and size up Monk, I got the second shock in that one minute. Monk's nose was bleeding, but that wasn't the thing that interested me most. It was the look in his eyes that got me. He looked hunted, or maybe baffled. He looked about as surprised and baffled as any guy I've ever seen.

Time and again I watched Monk storm into Pitcher as I stood there on the inner ring of the crowd. Monk would put his head down, and with both fists flying, sail into poor Pitch. It made me shudder at first just to see him charge and to watch the fists flying, but after a while it got funny. Because Pitch was never there. He'd tap Monk off balance, or step aside and let him charge by. I never saw anything like it in my life.

It was after one of those foolish charges, when Monk was standing there with that look in his eye, panting and wiping the blood off his nose, that somebody laughed. I looked up, and it was Star Collins who was laughing. He had Pitcher's glasses in his hand, and he was laughing hard. At Monk.

A second later everybody was laughing. I don't blame them, when you consider the look on Monk's face. They laughed and hollered and carried on, until finally Pitcher himself started to smile. I'm sure he thought they were laughing at him, because he's so used to being laughed at. And he did look funny himself out there in the center, come to think of it, with those awkward arms up and that earnest look on his face. So he put his arms down and he grinned.

"I can't hurt you, Monk," he said, "and you can't hurt me. I guess we're pretty funny at that."

Over in his corner Monk slowly put his hands down. He shook his head, then quickly reached for his handkerchief to stop the blood from his nose. "I guess we're pretty funny," he mumbled through the cloth.

Pitcher walked over to him, sticking out his hand. For a while they stood there shaking hands and then, by gosh, they laughed. Monk laughed so hard that some of his blood spattered on Pitch.

"Here's your glasses, Pitch," Star said while Monk was wiping his own blood off Pitcher. Star reached the glasses over and set them on Pitcher's nose. "And boy, can you box!"

"I'll say!" Monk said. For a second that look came back into his face, but he laughed it off. He put his hand on Pitcher's shoulder. "Let's go get a shower, Pitch," he invited. "We could both use one." And off they went.

I was the last one to leave. The crowd melted away the way crowds do, and I was standing there alone when Mr. Harper came out of the school building. He waved at me and said, "Hello, Robby."

"Hello, Mr. Harper," I said.

He never said another word, just kept walking up toward his house. But when he passed me, he slowly closed his left eye in an enormous wink.

Think About This:

1. Why did Robby *not* know what to say when Pitcher talked about his mother?
2. Why do you think Monk wanted to cheat?
3. Why do you think Mr. Harper didn't want Robby to tell anyone that he was watching the fight?
4. What might have happened to Pitcher if he had not known how to box?

More Than One Way

Sancho Panza, The Windmills, and Other Matters

(A selection from *Don Quixote* by Miguel de Cervantes)
Retold by James Reeves

Knights exist only in storybooks. But no one told that to Don Quixote. Instead of attending to his home, he spends his time reading romantic stories of knights in shining armor, witches, and giants. One day he decides to be a knight-errant, or wandering knight, in search of adventure. He finds a rusty suit of armor, a sword, and a thin old horse. People look at Don Quixote in his rusty armor and think he is crazy. He does not seem to belong in his day and age. Which has changed, Don Quixote or the world?

Don Quixote lay in bed, dreaming of knights and giants, and
sometimes calling out in his sleep. At this time, the priest and the
barber met with the housekeeper to decide what was best to be
done next. They decided to get a man to wall up the room in which
the books had been kept. Then the cause of all the trouble might
be forgotten.

"We must tell him," said the barber, "that someone came in
the night and took away his books, and even the library itself."

"Better still," said Quixote's niece, "if we say it was some evil
person who was his special enemy. He will believe that, for
certain."

This was done. A bricklayer was called in hurriedly to take
away the door of the library and put a wall in its place. When
Quixote woke up, he asked first for food and then his books.

"What books?" asked the housekeeper. "There are no such
things here, sir."

"Why, uncle," said his niece, "a terrible person, whose name
I do not know, came here last night and filled the house with
smoke. Then he must have carried away your books, together with
the library itself. There is no sign of them."

Quixote, after searching the house, said it must have been as they had told him. He swore there and then to get even with his enemy, the evil person who had come in the night and stolen his library.

During the next few days the priest tried to get Quixote to give up looking for adventures and stay at home. But Quixote had formed another plan.

He went down to the village and talked to a poor worker called Sancho Panza. He was a simple fellow with a wife and several children.

"Friend Sancho," said the knight, "I have need of a squire to go with me on my travels, to share my adventures and see to my needs. Will you go with me?"

Sancho Panza said he did not know how he could leave his family.

"If you come with me," said Quixote, "you shall have fame and glory. All the great knights of the past had their squires, and in the end they rewarded them for their service. Now I shall be sure of winning lands and wealth, and I shall make you ruler of some island. How would you like that? You shall be king. Your wife shall be queen. Your children shall be princes and princesses."

"As to that, sir," answered Sancho, "I'm not sure that my wife would make much of a queen. Still, I wouldn't half like to have an island of my own to be king of. So if your honor can promise me this, I'll go along with you, and gladly."

"Great!" cried Quixote. "We will set out at once. I will ride upon my fine horse Rosinante. You shall run by my side."

"As to that, your honor," said Sancho, "I'm no great hand at running. I'm not as fit as I was, and I've got a good-tempered donkey called Dapple who'll carry me a sight better than my own two legs."

Don Quixote was not at all sure that the brave knights of old would have allowed their squires to ride donkeys. Still, he gave in and said, "Very well, friend Sancho, I will allow you to ride your donkey. When I defeat some wandering knight, I shall present you with his mount."

So it was arranged. Quixote went home to repair his armor as best he might. Sancho got ready, too, and found a pair of saddlebags to carry food and extra clothes. Next day, without taking any leave of their families, knight and squire set off together across the plain in search of daring adventures.

They had not been riding long before there appeared up ahead thirty or forty great windmills.

"Aha!" cried Quixote, his eyes gleaming with the light of adventure. "Come, friend Sancho, and help me while I do battle against this army of great and mighty giants!"

"What giants, sir?" asked Sancho.

Just then a wind blew across the plain, and the sails of the windmills began to turn.

"See yonder," said Quixote. "There must be over thirty of them. They are waving their mighty arms as if to challenge us. I will charge against them single-handed. If you won't come with me, stay here and pray for my victory. You shall see what a brave and chivalrous act I shall do to this terrible army."

Sancho was certain there were no giants, but he could see that it was no good to argue. His master had already clapped spurs to Rosinante's sides and was preparing to charge against the windmills.

"Fly not, false cowards!" shouted Quixote. His lance shook before him as he rode nearer and nearer. "Perhaps you are the evil persons who stole my books! Now I shall have revenge upon you, not only for that deed, but for all the other terrible deeds that you have done to the people of this country."

Then he called upon Dulcinea, his ladylove, to aid him in his single-handed battle. He urged Rosinante to a gallop. His lance stuck through one of the sails of the nearest windmill. Both he and his horse were dragged toward it. Then the lance was broken to pieces. Don Quixote, thrown from his saddle, rolled across the plain.

Sancho Panza ran up to help his master.

"Oh, my goodness," he said, "now look what you've gone and done! I knew it was no good setting on a lot of harmless windmills. If I were you sir —"

"Silence, friend!" said Quixote. "Let not a squire question the deeds of his brave master. For I can see things that are hidden from your eyes!"

"Indeed, that is so," agreed Sancho. "But you scared me.

Honest, you did, sir. I really can't see as how charging one of those things is going to get us anywhere."

"Sancho," said Quixote, as he again mounted Rosinante, "it is the duty of every true knight to destroy all giants, dragons, and evil persons. If he fails to do so, he is unworthy of the title of knight."

"Very good, sir," said Sancho, "just as you say. But now you've destroyed the giants, what about a bite of dinner?"

"Not yet," said Quixote. "We must go on."

So they proceeded, Quixote on Rosinante and Sancho on Dapple, who was well loaded with saddlebags carrying the food Sancho dearly wanted to get at.

After a while night began to fall, and Quixote said they might rest under an oak tree. They got off their horses and Sancho gladly pulled out some food from one of the bags and began to help himself.

"Ah well," he said to himself, "it's not so bad, this wandering life — at least it's a change. And won't it be fun when I'm king of some island!"

But Quixote refused to eat. He seemed to have no interest in food and drink. Instead, he settled down to pass the night in thinking about his absent lady, the beautiful Dulcinea of Toboso. He had read that all true knights spend many sleepless hours in dreaming of their absent ladies. As for Sancho Panza, it was not long before he was sleeping soundly. Only his deep and peaceful snoring broke the silence of the night.

Next day they were up early. It was not long before they were once more riding across the plain. Soon a party of people were seen up ahead. When they came nearer, Quixote and Sancho could make out two large figures in black seated upon huge mules. They wore masks to keep the dust from their faces. They carried shades over their heads. They were attended by several country lads. Behind them was a coach carrying a lady and her friend on their way to Seville. Four or five men on horses and several mule riders were riding with them.

"Oho!" said Sancho to himself, as he saw his master looking toward the party. "More giants, I shouldn't wonder!"

Now the two men in black were no other than monks. But to Don Quixote they were evil persons who were carrying off some woman in the coach. The monks had, indeed, nothing to do with the ladies in the coach. They were simply riding in the same direction for company.

"See you those wicked magicians?" Quixote asked Sancho. "Look how your brave master goes to free those fair ladies whom they have taken. They are even now on their way to shut them up in the dungeon of their castle!"

"Oh, have a care, master," said Sancho. "I'll swear these are nothing but a pair of simple monks and no magicians, as you say."

"Shame upon you!" cried Quixote, drawing boldly up in the middle of the road. "Hold, evil persons!" he cried, as the monks came nearer. "Give up the unhappy princesses, or I shall wipe you from the face of the earth."

"Sir," said the nearest of the monks, "I promise you we know nothing of any princesses. We do but go peacefully on our way, bothering no one."

"You lie!" shouted Quixote. Without saying any more he charged full at the monk. The second monk, seeing what was going on, rode to one side as quickly as he could. The first monk could only avoid Quixote's weapon by falling off his mule. Seeing his enemy so easily defeated, Quixote rode up to the coach to offer his help to the ladies. Sancho got down from his mule beside the fallen monk and began to help himself to his clothes.

"Surely," said he to himself, "these are the spoils of battle. My master has defeated this fellow. I am entitled to his clothes."

But the monk's servants, seeing that the terrible Don Quixote

was not looking, stepped up to Sancho and began beating him. They first knocked him to the ground in defense of their master. Then they helped the monk to his feet. The monk got upon his mule and rode off to join his friend, without waiting to see what happened next.

"Fair ladies," said Quixote to the two in the coach. "You are indeed lucky in being saved from these four by the thrice-famous flower of chivalry, Don Quixote of La Mancha. Ladies, I beg of you, go now to Toboso and pay your humble respects to the beautiful Dulcinea. She is the soul and guiding star of him who has served you!"

"We shall do no such thing!" said one of the men with the ladies. "Toboso is far out of our way. We're going to Seville. And if you'll kindly get out of the way, you old fool, we'll be on our road!"

This speech was too much for Quixote.

"If you were a man," said he, "I should fight with you. As it is, slave, I order you to be silent. Do not get in the way of something that does not concern you."

For answer the man raised his sword and gave Quixote a blow. Had it not been for Quixote's armor, the man would certainly have split Quixote down to the waist. This so angered the knight that he felled him to the ground.

At this the ladies in the coach begged Quixote to spare their poor servant.

"This will I do, ladies," answered Quixote, "on one condition, as is required by the laws of chivalry. See that your servant goes instantly to Toboso and presents himself up to the beautiful Dulcinea. She may do what she will with him."

The ladies promised that it should be as he said. The servant was then allowed to get to his feet. Then the whole party set off along the road.

When they had gone, Sancho, who had now recovered from his beating, came up to Don Quixote and said:

"Now, master, what about giving me that island? Surely it's time I was made a king."

"Not yet, friend Sancho," answered Quixote. "There is much to be done before that can be. Let us again mount our faithful beasts and be on our way."

Sancho Panza shrugged his shoulders and did as his master had said.

Think About This:

1. Why did the people in Don Quixote's household wall up the door to the library?
2. How does Don Quixote describe his horse Rosinante? How would you describe it?
3. Why do you think Sancho Panza went along with Don Quixote?
4. What did Don Quixote do instead of sleep when the two stopped to rest under the oak tree? Why?

Tough Hombres, Tougher Pudding

James Emmit McCauley

There's no doubt about it, life on the frontier was tough. One of the toughest times for the cowboy cook in this story was the day he had to "build" a pudding. Just how hard can cooking a pudding be? Well, times have changed, as you will find out.

One winter when I was working on the XT Ranch, it fell to my lot to do the cooking, or most of it.

For Christmas I decided I'd try to cook up something extra. We had plenty of most everything you could find to eat in a grocery store. First I tried to make some apple pies. In the place of using lard for shortening, I put in tallow. I put in plenty, too. When I rolled out the crust, the tallow became hard. It was full of lumps. But I made the pies just the same. They ought to have been very good. I put in every kind of flavoring they had at the ranch. All the cowboys from the neighboring ranches who visited us said they were hard to beat. But you can fix up any sort of stuff and call it *pie*. Sink it in the Rio Grande River, and every cowboy in New Mexico would be drowned diving after it.

After the pie racket, old John Cummins got after me to cook something he called *English pudding*. I put in very near everything there was, such as squad berries, yellow currants, rice, and dried grapes. But I never put in any baking powder. The result was it didn't swell any. I had cooked enough to know that anything that has flour in it has to swell or 'tis no good. Anyhow, I got it mixed up and ready after a while. Then I didn't have any sack to put it in. So I tied it up in a piece of deer skin and boiled it for two whole days. That ought to have been enough. It certainly had all the chance any fair pudding could ask for swelling and showing its strength. But it didn't seem to come up, not a bit. I got sick of seeing and smelling it after the second day and took it out of the pot.

Cummins said it ought to be sort of cured before it was ready to be eaten. I laid it out on top of the dobe ranch house where it could enjoy the sun. It sure got cured. I guess it was not used to being in the sun of a day and cold wind of a night. It must have been kind of hard on the pudding. I forgot all about it. When I did think of it and went to bring it in, it had fallen off of the house and was laying in a snow drift. I had to peel the hide off with a chisel.

I kind of mistrusted it a whole lot when I got a square look at it. It looked like it had a mean disposition and meant murder. While I was getting dinner I worried a piece loose from it to get a taste, and I liked to have never got it off my teeth. Even Cummins could not eat any of it and nobody that came along could bear to eat it.

We kept the thing for a kind of an ornament after that until one day it rolled off the table and liked to have broke my foot. I threw it out in the yard, and it kind of knocked around for itself for a while. There was an old magpie around the ranch, a fine old fellow. We had made a pet of him and taught him lots of tricks. The day the pudding was thrown out, he found it and pecked a little piece off. We never suspected he could talk. But when he got that taste in his mouth, he screamed, "What have I done!" The next morning we found him dead. That summer a fellow came down by the ranch hunting Indian relics for some museum back East. He

worked around for two whole days digging in some ruins out by the corral, getting old jugs and things. One day he came across that old pudding out in the yard.

"My, my!" he says. "How lucky I must be."

"What is it?" I asked him. And what do you think? He told me it was one of those stones the Aztecs had used to pound their corn with to make bread. He told me he would give me five dollars for it. I was taking him up on it when old Cummins had to put in and tell him it was no stone but a pudding. The fellow asked me if I'd have taken the money. I told him yes. I've paid good money for things I would not have wanted at all if I had known better. Anyway, that isn't the point. I never could see the use of spoiling a good joke just for nothing. Besides, I never got paid for building that pudding. If Cummins had kept his mouth shut that pudding would have had a nice, easy job right now in some big museum back East. People would see it and think it had beat up hundreds of bushels of corn for Indians before Columbus discovered America.

After the professor left, since he had brought the wonderful pudding in and used it for a footstool, we put it against the door and used it to keep the door open. After we had peeled it with a chisel and could not eat it, we named it old Rough and Ready. One day it got too close to the fire. When I went in the room it had melted and had run all over the hearth. It was the stickiest outfit I ever set my two peepers on. Gus de Cordova came in with an old tobacco box. He picked it up with a shovel and took it out and

buried the remains. One day I happened around, and he had put up a board with this inscription on it:

HERE LIES OLD IRONSIDES

BY ITS HAND SIX MEN WERE SAVED FROM DEATH

(that was when we could not eat it, Gus explained)

ALSO KILLED ONE MAGPIE

ALSO FOOLED ONE PROFESSOR

AND IT DID ITS DUTY AND LIES HERE

I laughed until I was sick. But from then until this very now I never built another pudding.

What Do You Do If You Don't Have a Bathtub?

Ruth Jaeger Buntain

How would you get clean if you didn't have a bathtub or shower? Animals must clean themselves in ways that their surroundings provide.

Most of you know that birds take baths. Sometimes they bathe in puddles, sometimes in dust or sand holes, sometimes in the snow. But there are many other kinds of "baths" that animals take.

The vulture takes a sunbath in a tree. Sitting on a high branch, it spreads its wings so that sunshine can reach all its feathers. Since vultures eat dead flesh, they pick up many germs on their bodies. The warm sunshine helps to kill the germs.

Reprinted from *Ranger Rick's Nature Magazine*, by permission of the publisher, the National Wildlife Federation.

Kangaroo rats take dust baths. If you are in the desert where this tiny yellow-brown animal lives, you may see it rolling in the sand. As it rolls over and over, the sand acts as a brush to clean its fur.

Even the earthworm takes a bath. It does its bathing at night. When the earth is still and most animals are asleep, the worm crawls out of its home under the ground. It eats and drinks and takes a bath in the dew.

The elephant takes a shower. It walks out into the water and sucks up water into its trunk and sprays it all over its body. If a baby elephant is near, it gets sprayed, too.

But most animal mothers don't spray their babies to get them clean. They lick them with their tongues.

That's what a mother tiger does. Her tongue is rough and makes a good scrubber. She licks off any dirt that may be on her cub.

A cat uses its tongue to wash, too. Because a cat's body stretches, it can reach almost everywhere with its tongue.

The parts it can't reach, the cat cleans in a different way. It wets a paw with its tongue and rubs the paw over its fur. Watch a pet cat do this when it washes its face.

Dogs most often get clean by scratching. This gets rid of the loose hairs. They don't often take a water bath — on their own, anyway. Too much water makes a dog's skin dry out and it may crack.

When children take baths, they sometimes forget to clean their ears. But bats don't forget. Their ears must always be clean, because they find their way by listening to sounds (echo location).

A bat puts the thumb of its winged front "hand" in its ear and turns it around and around to loosen the dirt. The rest of its body is cleaned with its long pink tongue.

A rabbit also remembers to clean its ears. It pushes them forward with a foot so that its tongue can reach them. It cleans its feet by shaking each one to loosen the dirt, and then licking it.

Squirrels are mostly concerned with cleaning their tails. They spend hours combing their tails, but for good reason. A squirrel's tail acts as a parachute when it jumps and as a "balancing pole" when it runs along branches. In winter, asleep in its nest, it wraps itself in a warm tail "blanket."

Just as human beings use combs to keep their hair smooth, so do many animals. After bathing, the duckbill platypus combs its fur with a long claw until it's smooth and in place.

Bears use claw "combs," too. They sharpen their claws on stumps and tree trunks. This keeps their "combs" sharp. Claws are also the bear's main weapons of defense.

Birds sometimes use claw "combs." But more often they comb, or preen, with their bills. As a matter of fact, they preen most of the day. Some birds run their bills over their feathers to make them lie in place. Their bills are often used to spread oil from a special gland. This keeps water from soaking into their feathers.

A hummingbird was once seen cleaning its "comb" after using it. The hummingbird scraped and rubbed its bill with its claws until the bill was clean and shiny.

Even insects have ways of keeping clean. Bees have "combs" on their front legs with which they clean their antennae.

Ants have antennae-cleaning "brushes" on their "arms." After cleaning their antennae, they lick the "brushes" clean.

The "big boss" baboon is taken care of by other baboons. They act as servants and pick their leader clean.

Another animal that doesn't clean itself is the moray eel. But it needs cleaning to rid its mouth of sea lice. So it swims to a reef in the ocean where small wrasses are darting about. These finger-size fish seem to be trying to get attention. They seem to be calling out, "Here we are! At your service!" The eel opens its huge

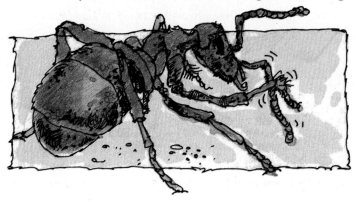

mouth, full of sharp teeth, and some of the little fish swim into it and start cleaning. When they are finished, the eel swims away.

Whether it is by splashing, rolling, spraying, licking, scratching, or shaking, almost all animals keep clean. They seem to know, just as people do, that one of the ways to stay healthy is to be clean.

Think About This:

1. How does a kangaroo rat bathe?
2. Why does a bat clean its ears?
3. With what does a bear comb its hair?
4. How and why do birds clean their feathers?
5. From what you know about each of these animals, tell how you think their cleaning habits show that they have adapted to their surroundings.

The Medicine Bag

Driving Hawk

There is more than one way to live. But what if your grand-father lives on a reservation? When Joe Iron Shell comes from the Sioux Indian reservation for a visit, Martin must deal with some very mixed-up feelings. Can he live up to the pride that he has always felt for his Indian heritage and for his Indian great-grandfather? Or will he change?

My kid sister Cheryl and I always boasted about our Sioux grandpa, Joe Iron Shell. Our friends, who had always lived in the city and only knew about Indians from movies and TV, were impressed by our stories. Maybe we stretched the truth and made Grandpa sound glamorous, but when we'd return home to Iowa after our yearly summer visit to Grandpa we always had some exciting tale to tell.

We always had some real Sioux gift to show our listeners. On one visit Grandpa gave me a small, round, flat, skin drum with a painting on it of a warrior riding a horse. He taught me a real Sioux chant to sing while I beat the drum with a leather-covered stick that had a feather on the end. Man, that really got their attention.

We never showed our Grandpa's picture. Not that we weren't proud of him, but because we knew that the exciting tales we told didn't go with the real thing. Our friends would have laughed at the picture, because Grandpa wasn't tall and stately like TV Indians. His hair wasn't in braids, but hung in gray strings on his neck and he was old. He was our great-grandfather. He didn't live in a tipi, but all by himself in a part log, part tar-paper shed on the Rosebud Reservation in South Dakota. So when Grandpa came to visit us, I was so worried I could've died.

There are a lot of fancy little dogs in our neighborhood, but they usually barked only at the mail carrier from the safety of their own yards. Now it sounded as if a whole pack were barking together in one place.

I got up and walked to the street to see what was causing all the noise. About a block away I saw a crowd of little kids yelling, with dogs barking and growling around someone who was walking down the middle of the street.

In the center of the strange parade was a man wearing a tall

black hat. I felt cold and hot at the same time. "Oh no!" I whispered. "It's Grandpa!"

I stood on the curb. I couldn't move even though I wanted to run and hide. Then I got mad when I saw how the yippy dogs were snapping at the old man's baggy pant legs and how weakly he poked them away with his cane. "Stupid dogs," I said as I ran to help Grandpa.

"Grandpa," I said and felt pretty dumb when my voice cracked. I reached for his beat-up old tin case, which was tied shut with a rope. But he set it down right in the street and shook my hand.

"*Hau, Takoza*, Grandchild," he greeted me gravely in Sioux.

All I could do was stand there with the whole neighborhood watching and shake the hand of the leather-brown old man. I saw how his gray hair straggled from under his big black hat, which had a limp feather in its crown. His rumpled black suit hung like a sack over his stooped frame. As he shook my hand, his coat fell open, showing beneath it a bright-red satin shirt with a beaded bolo tie under the collar. His outfit wasn't out of place on the reservation, but it sure was here. I wanted to sink right through the street.

"Hi," I muttered with my head down. I tried to pull my hand away when I felt his bony hand trembling. When I looked up I could see from his face how tired he was. I felt like crying. I picked up Grandpa's case, took his arm, and guided him up the drive to our house.

Mom was standing on the steps.

"*Hau*, Marie," he said as he shook Mom's hand. She smiled and took his other arm.

As we helped him up the steps the door banged open and Cheryl came bursting out of the house. She was all smiles and was so openly glad to see Grandpa that I was ashamed of how I felt.

"Grandpa!" she yelled happily. "You came to see us."

Grandpa smiled and Mom and I let go of him as he stretched out his arms to my 10-year-old sister.

"*Wicincala,* little girl," he greeted her and then collapsed.

He had fainted. Mom and I carried him into her sewing room, where we had an extra bed.

After we had Grandpa on the bed, Mom stood there helplessly patting his shoulder.

"Shouldn't we call the doctor, Mom?" I asked, since she didn't seem to know what to do.

"Yes," she agreed with a sigh. "You make Grandpa comfortable, Martin."

I knew Grandpa wouldn't want to have Mom undress him, but I didn't want to, either. He was so thin and frail that it was easy to slip his coat off. When I took off his tie and opened his shirt collar, I felt a small leather bag that hung from a cord around his neck. I left it alone and moved to remove his boots. The scuffed old cowboy boots were tight and he moaned as I jerked them off.

I put the boots on the floor and saw why they fit so tight. Each one was stuffed with money.

Mom came back with a bowl of water. "The doctor thinks Grandpa is suffering from heat exhaustion," she explained, as she bathed Grandpa's face. Mom gave a big sigh, "*Oh hinh,* Martin. How do you suppose he got here?"

We found out after the doctor's visit.

Between sips of soup Grandpa told us of his journey. Soon after our visit to him Grandpa decided that he would like to see where his only living family lived and what our home was like. Besides, he added sheepishly, he was lonesome after we left.

I knew everybody felt as bad as I did — especially Mom. Mom

was all Grandpa had left. So even after she married my dad, and after Cheryl and I were born, Mom made sure that every summer we spent a week with Grandpa.

I never thought that Grandpa would be lonely after our visits, and none of us noticed how old and weak he had become. But Grandpa knew and so he came to us. He had traveled on buses for two and a half days. When he arrived in the city, tired and stiff from sitting for so long, he set out, walking, to find us.

He had stopped to rest on the steps of some building downtown and a policeman found him. The policeman, Grandpa said, was a good man who took him to the bus stop and told the driver to let Grandpa out at Bell View Drive. After Grandpa got off the bus, he started walking again. But he couldn't see the house numbers on the other side when he walked on the sidewalk, so he walked in the middle of the street. That's when all the little kids and dogs followed him.

I knew everybody felt as bad as I did. Yet I was proud of this 86-year-old man, who had never been away from the reservation, having the courage to travel so far alone.

"You found the money in my boots?" he asked Mom.

"Martin did," she answered.

"The money is what I've saved for a long time — a hundred dollars — for my funeral. But you take it now to buy groceries so that I won't be a trouble to you while I am here."

"No, Grandpa," Dad said. "We are honored to have you with us and you will never be trouble to us. I am only sorry that we never thought to bring you home with us this summer and spare you this long trip."

Grandpa was pleased. "Thank you," he answered. "But do not feel bad that you didn't bring me with you, for I would not have come then. It was not time." He said this in such a way that no one could argue with him. To Grandpa and the Sioux, he once told me, a thing would be done when it was the right time to do it, and that's the way it was.

"Also," Grandpa went on, looking at me, "I have come because it is soon time for Martin to have the medicine bag."

We all knew what that meant. Grandpa thought he was going to die and he had to follow the tradition of his family to pass the medicine bag, along with its history, to the oldest male child.

I didn't know what to say. I had the same hot and cold feeling that I had when I first saw Grandpa in the street. The medicine bag was the dirty leather pouch I had found around his neck. "I could never wear such a thing," I almost said aloud. I thought of having my friends see it at the swimming pool, and could imagine the smart things they would say. But I just swallowed hard and took a step toward the bed. I knew I would have to take it.

But Grandpa was tired. "Not now, Martin," he said, waving his hand to dismiss us, "it is not time. Now I will sleep."

So that's how Grandpa came to be with us for two months. My friends kept asking to come see the old man, but I put them off. I told myself that I didn't want them laughing at Grandpa. But even as I made excuses I knew it wasn't Grandpa that I was afraid they'd laugh at.

Nothing bothered Cheryl about bringing her friends to see Grandpa. Every day after school started there'd be a bunch of little girls or boys crowded around the old man.

Grandpa would smile in his gentle way and answer their questions, or he'd tell them stories. The kids listened in awed silence. Those little guys thought Grandpa was great.

Finally, one day after school my friends came home with me because nothing I said stopped them.

When we got to my house Grandpa was sitting on the patio. He had on his red shirt, but today he also wore a fringed leather vest sewn on top with beads. Instead of his cowboy boots he wore beaded moccasins. Of course, he had his old black hat on — he was almost never without it. But it had been brushed and the feather in the beaded headband was standing up proudly, its tip a brighter white. His hair lay in silver strands over the red shirt collar.

I stared just as my friends did, and I heard one of them murmur, "Wow!"

Grandpa looked up and when his eyes met mine, they twinkled as if he were laughing inside. He nodded to me and my face got all hot. I could tell that he had known all along I was afraid he'd embarrass me in front of my friends.

"*Hau, hoksilas*, boys," he greeted and held out his hand.

My friends passed in a single file and shook his hand as I introduced them. They were so polite I almost laughed.

"You look fine, Grandpa," I said as the guys sat on the lawn chairs or on the floor.

"*Hanh*, yes," he agreed. "When I woke up this morning it seemed the right time to dress in the good clothes. I knew that my grandson would be bringing his friends."

"You guys want some lemonade or something?" I offered. No one answered. They were listening to Grandpa as he started telling how he'd killed the deer from which his vest was made.

Grandpa did most of the talking while my friends were there. I was so proud of him and amazed at how respectfully quiet my friends were. Mom had to chase them home at supper time. As they left they shook Grandpa's hand again and said to me:

"Martin, he's really great!"

"Yeah, man! Don't blame you for keeping him to yourself."

"Can we come back?"

But after they left, Mom said, "No more visitors for a while,

Martin. Grandpa won't admit it, but he is still not very strong."

All night I had strange dreams about thunder and lightning on a high hill. From a distance I heard the slow beat of a drum. At school it seemed as if the day would never end and, when it finally did, I ran home.

Grandpa was in his room, sitting on the bed. The shades were down and the place was dim and cool. I sat on the floor in front of Grandpa, but he didn't even look at me. After what seemed a long time he spoke.

"I sent your mother and sister away. What you will hear today is only for your ears. What you will receive is only for your hands." He fell silent and I felt shivers down my back.

"My father in his youth," Grandpa began, "made a vision quest to find a spirit guide for his life. You cannot understand how it was in that time, when the great Teton Sioux were first made to stay on the reservation. There was a strong need for guidance from *Wakantanka*, the Great Spirit. But too many of the young men were filled with despair and hate. They thought it was hopeless to search for a vision. But my father held to the old ways.

"He carefully prepared for his search with a purifying sweat bath and then he went alone to a high butte top to fast and pray. After three days he received his sacred dream — in which he found, after long searching, the white man's iron. He did not understand his dream of finding something belonging to the white people, for in that time they were the enemy. When he came down from the butte to cleanse himself at the stream below, he found the remains of a campfire and the broken shell of an iron kettle. This sign seemed to bear out his dream. He took a piece of the iron for his medicine bag.

"He returned to his village, where he told his dream to the wise old men of the tribe. They gave him the name *Iron Shell*, but

neither did they understand the meaning of the dream. This first Iron Shell kept the piece of iron with him at all times, and believed that it protected him from the evils of those unhappy days.

"Then a terrible thing happened to Iron Shell. He and several other young men were taken from their homes by the soldiers and sent far away to a white man's boarding school. At first Iron Shell fought against the teachers' attempts to change him, and he did not try to learn. One day it was his turn to work in the school's blacksmith shop. As he walked into the place, he knew that his medicine had brought him there to learn and work with the white man's iron.

"Iron Shell became a blacksmith and worked at the trade when he returned to the reservation. All of his life he treasured the medicine bag. When he was old, and I was a man, he gave it to me, for no one made the vision quest anymore."

Grandpa quit talking and I stared in shock as he covered his face with his hands. His shoulders were shaking with quiet sobs and I looked away until he began to speak again.

"I kept the bag until my son, your mother's father, was a man and had to leave us to fight in the war across the ocean. I gave him the bag, for I believed it would protect him in battle, but he did not take it with him. He was afraid that he would lose it. He died in a far-off place."

Again Grandpa was still and I felt his sorrow around me.

He unbuttoned his shirt, pulled out the leather pouch, and lifted it over his head. He held it in his hand, turning it over and over as if memorizing how it looked.

"In the bag," he said as he opened it and removed two objects, "is the broken shell of the iron kettle, a pebble from the butte, and a piece of the sacred sage." He held the pouch upside down and dust drifted down.

"After the bag is yours, you must put a piece of sage inside it and never open it again until you pass it on to your son." He put the pebble and the piece of iron back into the bag, and tied it.

I stood up, somehow knowing I should. Grandpa slowly rose from the bed and stood up straight in front of me, holding the bag before my face. I closed my eyes and waited for him to slip it over my head. But he spoke.

"No, you need not wear it." He placed the soft leather bag in my right hand and closed my other hand over it. "It would not be right to wear it in this time and place where no one will understand. Put it safely away until you are again on the reservation. Wear it then, when you find the sacred sage."

Grandpa turned and sat again on the bed. Weakly he leaned his head against the pillow. "Go," he said, "I will sleep now."

"Thank you, Grandpa," I said softly and left with the bag in my hands.

That night Mom and Dad took Grandpa to the hospital. Two weeks later I stood alone on the lonely prairie of the reservation and put the sacred sage in my bag.

Think About This:

1. Why was Martin embarrassed when Joe Iron Shell came to visit?
2. When Martin's friends finally met Joe Iron Shell, how did they act?
3. In what ways did Grandpa prove to be a very wise old man?
4. Why do you think that Grandpa chose this visit to give the medicine bag to Martin?

Why Did You Say That?

The world has changed in many ways, and it keeps on changing all the time. The language that people use changes. New words and idioms appear and disappear. The meanings of words change, too. This selection, "Why Did You Say That?," tells about the meaning of the word "maverick" and the idioms "pull up stakes," "start from scratch," and "off your base."

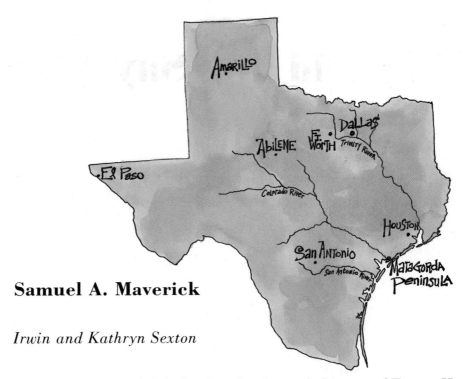

Samuel A. Maverick

Irwin and Kathryn Sexton

Samuel Maverick helped make the early history of Texas. He was one of the state's leaders in business and politics. But when people hear the name Maverick, they often think first of the word "maverick." Dictionaries give two meanings: (1) An animal without a brand. (2) Someone who won't join any kind of group. Sam Maverick was not a rancher, even though he owned a ranch. He was quiet. He was wise and fair in politics. How did he happen to have his name used either for cows without brands or for self-willed persons? The story is interesting.

In 1847 Maverick accepted four hundred head of cattle instead of twelve hundred dollars someone owed him. He kept the cattle on his ranch on the Matagorda Peninsula, in Texas. Maverick moved back to San Antonio. His servant Jack was left in charge of the ranch and the cattle. Jack didn't care about his work and let the cattle stray.

In 1854, Maverick had the cattle moved to Conquista Ranch, which he also owned, on the bank of the San Antonio River. Many of the cattle were not branded when they were moved. Marking was needed to show who owned the cattle that were not kept in fences. Cattle without marks could be taken by anyone. Sam Maverick's cattle were wild. They strayed because Jack did not watch them.

The lost cattle caused trouble when Maverick sold the cattle to A. Toutant Beauregard some two years later in 1856. Part of the deal was that Beauregard had to round up all the cattle. It was hard work. Whenever a calf without a mark was found, the workers took it for Maverick's, or, as they began to say, "a maverick." They marked all of these.

Cowboys told the story about the maverick cattle as they moved around the country. The term "maverick" was soon used by people all over the United States for any cattle without marks.

Later, the word "maverick" came to mean people who do not go along with others. These people stray from the "mark" of a group or an accepted way of thinking.

Some Idioms

Charles Earle Funk

To "pull up stakes" means to move from a place. This saying goes back to colonial days in New England. If settlers did not like their land, they pulled up the boundary stakes and left. Some

of them returned to England. Others stayed to settle on other land of their own choosing. The earliest record of anyone using this term was between 1638 and 1640. An English lawyer, Thomas Lechford, wrote to a friend in England, ". . . but am plucking up stakes, with as much speed as I may, if so be I may be so happy as to arrive in Ireland . . ."

To "start from scratch" means to start something from the beginning. The term comes from the sports world, from a race in which *scratch* is the starting mark. So someone who starts from scratch starts with nothing.

To be "off your base" means what it says in baseball. It means that a runner is a few steps away from the bag or base in order to get a head start to the next one. But *base* can also stand for something that supports a person. If someone says you are "off your base," it means you are not thinking straight.

In the last selection, you read about changes in words and in the ways they are used. The poetry on the following pages will show you that poetry has also changed. As you read these poems, think about how poetry can change the ways in which you see the everyday world.

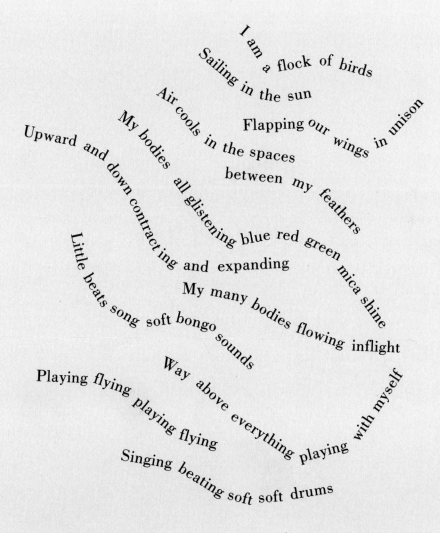

I am a flock of birds
Sailing in the sun
Flapping our wings in unison
Air cools in the spaces
My bodies all glistering
between my feathers
Upward and down contracting and expanding blue red green mica shine
My many bodies flowing inflight
Little beats song soft bongo sounds
Way above everything playing with myself
Playing flying playing flying
Singing beating soft soft drums

Meg Wilson

The Sand Dunes

The sand dunes looked like they had been autographed by the wind.

Pamela Swain

How Everything Happens
(Based on a Study of the Wave)

```
                                        happen.
                                      to
                                    up
                              stacking
                          is
                        something
When nothing is happening

When it happens
                something
                      pulls
                          back
                              not
                                to
                                  happen.

When                              has happened.
        pulling back        stacking up
                    happens

            has happened                            stacks up.
When it              something              nothing
                        pulls back while

Then nothing is happening.

                                  happens.
                                and
                          forward
                      pushes
                    up
              stacks
        something
Then
```

May Swenson

Sound of Sunshine, Sound of Rain

Florence Parry Heide

Close your eyes. What do you hear? Can you hear colors?—soft colors, loud colors? The boy in this story is blind, but he knows much about the world around him. He knows of colors. He knows of loud water and still water and plain water. Imagine yourself in his place as you read. Listen closely to the sounds of sunshine and the sounds of rain. You may decide that there is more than one way to see the world.

It must be morning, for I hear the morning voices. I have been dreaming of a sound that whispers *Follow me, Follow me,* but not in words. I follow the sound up and up until I feel I am floating in the air.

Now I am awake, and I listen to the voices.

My mother's voice is warm and soft as a pillow.

My sister's voice is little and sharp and high, like needles flying in the air.

I do not listen to the words but to the sound. Low, high, low, high, soft, hard, soft, hard, and then the sounds coming together at the same time and making a new sound. And with it all, the sharp sounds of my sister's heels putting holes in what I hear.

Then I hear the slamming of kitchen drawers and the banging of pans, and there is no more talking.

My bed is in the living room. I reach out to feel whether my mother has laid my clothes on the chair beside my bed. They are there, and I feel the smoothness and the roughness of them.

I reach under the chair to find which shoes my mother has put there. They are my outside shoes, not my slippers, so today must be a warm day. Maybe I can go to the park. I tap my good luck song on the wall beside my bed.

I put my feet on the floor and feel the cool wood and curl my toes against it.

Then it is four steps to the table, then around the table, touching the chairs, and then seven steps to the window. I put my cheek against the window, and I can feel the warm sun. Now I am sure I can go to the park, if my sister has time to take me on her way to class.

I take my clothes into the bathroom, and I wash and dress there. Hot water, cold water, soapy water, plain water, loud water, still water. Then I make sure I have turned the faucets tight. I make sure I have buttoned all of my buttons the right way, or my sister will be cross, and maybe not have time to take me to the park.

I tap my good luck song against the door before I open it.

When I open the door, I hear the voices again. My sister's voice is like scissors cutting away at my mother's voice.

I sit at the table, and my mother gives me my breakfast. I breathe on the hot chocolate so I can feel it on my face coming back warm. I drink just a little at a time so I can keep holding the warm cup.

"Eat while it's hot," says my sister to me, loud.

"Does he have to be so slow?" says my sister to my mother in her quiet voice. My sister thinks because I cannot see that maybe I cannot hear very well, and she talks loud to me, and soft when she does not want me to hear, but I hear.

"You spilled," says my sister, loud.

"I can't be late," she says in her quiet voice to my mother. "Everybody's always late but me, and I won't be late."

After breakfast I go over to the window again, and when I put my cheek against the glass it is warmer than before, so today will be a good day. I tap my good luck song against the window.

My sister says she will take me to the park on her way to class. She gives me my jacket and tells me to wait for her outside on the steps.

I go down the outside steps. There are seven steps. Seven is my most magic number. Seven up, seven down, seven up, seven down. I go up and down, waiting for my sister.

My sister comes out. She takes my hand. She walks very fast, but I can still count the steps to the park, and I can still remember the turns. Someday I can go there by myself. I listen to the street noises and try to sort them out.

My sister's hand is not soft. I can feel her nails, little and sharp, like her voice, and I listen to her heels making holes in all the other sounds.

The park seems a long way off.

When we get to the park we go first to the bench. She waits to make sure I remember my way in the park. Fourteen steps to the bubbler. Around the bubbler, twenty steps to the curb.

I go back to the bench. I try to hurry so my sister won't have to wait long and be cross. Now seventeen steps to the phone booth, four benches on the way, and I touch them all. Then I come back to the bench.

My sister puts money in my pocket so I can telephone.

She talks to me and to herself.

"Filthy park," she says, and it is as if she were stepping on the words, "No grass. Trees in cages. Since when do benches and old newspapers make a park?" She pulls my jacket to straighten it.

Now she is gone and I have my morning in the sun.

I try each bench, but mine is still the best one.

I go to the bubbler and press my mouth against the water and feel it on my tongue, soft and warm. I put my finger on the place where the water comes out and walk around and around the bubbler, and then I try to find my bench. It is one of my games. I have many games.

I walk over to the telephone booth, touching the four benches on the way. I stand inside the booth. I feel to see whether there is any money in the telephone, but there is none. My sister says I should always check the telephone for money, but I have never found any.

I practice dialing our number so I will be sure I have it right. Then I put my dime in and call. I let it ring two times and then I hang up and get my dime back. My sister says that way my mother will know I am all right.

I blow on the glass, and it blows back to me. I tap my good luck song on it and go back to my bench.

I play one of my games. I listen to every sound and think if that sound would be able to do something to me, what it would do. Some sounds would scratch me; some would pinch me; some would push me. Some would carry me, some would crush me, and some would rock me.

I am sitting on my bench tapping my good luck song with my shoes when I hear the bells of an ice-cream truck. I feel the money in my pocket. I have the dime, and I also have a bigger one. I know I have enough for an ice-cream bar.

I walk out to the curb, touching the cages around the trees. I wait until the bells sound near, and I wave.

He stops. He is near enough for me to touch his cart. I hold out my money.

Now I feel him seeing me, but he does not take my money.

"Here," I say, but he does not take the money from me.

"Guess what?" he says, and his voice is soft and kind as fur. "Every tenth kid wins a free ice-cream bar, and you're the lucky one today."

I can feel him getting off his cart and going around to open the place where he keeps his ice-cream bars. I can feel him putting one near my hand, and I take it.

I start back to my bench.

"You gonna be okay by yourself now?" the ice-cream man calls, so I know he is seeing me.

I sit on the bench. I listen for the sound of his cart starting up, and his bells ringing, but I can only hear the other sounds, the regular ones.

Then I hear him walking over to my bench.

I am sorry, because I only want to feel the ice cream and see how long I can make it last. I do not want anyone to sit with me now. I am afraid I will spill it, and he will see me.

He starts to talk, and his voice is soft as a sweater.

His name is Abram. He tells me about the park.

My sister says the trees are in cages because if they weren't in cages, they wouldn't stay in such a terrible park, they'd just get up and go somewhere pretty.

Abram says the trees are in cages to keep them safe so they can grow to be big and tall. "Like sides on a crib for a baby, keeping him from falling and hurting himself," says Abram.

My sister says the park is ugly and dirty.

Abram says there are a few little bits of paper, and a couple of cans and some bottles, but he says he can squint up his eyes and all those things lying around shine like flowers. Abram says you see what you want to see.

My sister says that the park is just for poor folks and that no one would ever come here if they had a chance to go anywhere else.

Abram says the park is just for lucky people, like him and me.
He says the people who come to this park can see things inside
themselves, instead of just what their eyes tell them.

After a while Abram goes away. He says he will come back and
look for me tomorrow. I hear his ice-cream bells go farther and
farther away until I do not hear them anymore.

While I am waiting for my sister to come for me, I fall asleep on
the bench.

I have a good dream. I dream that Abram lifts me so I can
touch the leaves of a tree. All of the leaves are songs, and they fall
around me and cover me. I am warm and soft under the songs.

My sister shakes me awake. "You'll catch cold lying here,"
she says.

The next day while I am sitting on my bench, I hear the ice-cream bells, and I walk out to the curb, touching the cages of the trees as I go. Abram gives me an ice-cream bar, and we walk together back to the bench. I do not have to touch the cages because I am with him.

After I finish my ice-cream bar, Abram gives me some paper clips so I can feel them in my pocket. He shows me how I can twist them to make little shapes.

After he leaves, I feel them. There are seven paper clips.

That night I dream that someone is gathering in a big net everything in the world that makes a sound, and I am tumbled in the net and my sister shakes me awake.

"Stop thrashing around," she says. "You're all tangled up in the blanket."

The next day Abram brings me a balloon.

I can feel it round and tight. It tugs at the string.

Abram says some balloons are filled with something special that makes them want to fly away, up to the sun, and this balloon is filled with that something special.

He says some people are filled with something special that makes them pull and tug, too, trying to get up and away from where they are.

His voice is like a kitten curled on my shoulder.

He tells me my balloon is red, and then he tells me about colors.

He says colors are just like sounds. Some colors are loud, and some colors are soft, and some are big and some are little, and some are sharp and some are tender, just like sounds, just like music.

What is the best color, I wonder?

He says all colors are the same, as far as that goes.

There isn't a best color, says Abram. There isn't a good color or a bad color.

Colors are just on the outside. They aren't important at all. They're just covers for things, like a blanket.

Color don't mean a thing, says Abram.

When my sister comes, she asks me where I got my balloon. I tell her about my friend.

I hold onto the string of my balloon while we walk.

We stop at a store. When we go in, I hold my balloon against me so it won't get hurt.

The store feels crowded. I hear a lady's voice. It sounds as if she was squeezing it out of her like the last bit of toothpaste in a tube.

The lady's voice says, "Better wait on this black lady first."

My sister takes my hand and pulls me away. I hold my balloon tight.

"So we're black," says my sister to me as she pulls me along. "So what else is new? I've heard it a million times. I guess I heard it before I was even born."

"Abram says color don't mean a thing," I say.

My sister drags me along. I can tell by her hand that she's mad.

"What does he know? Is he black, your friend?" she asks.

"I don't know," I say.

"You don't even know if your friend is black or not," says my sister. "I wish everyone in the whole world was blind!" she cries.

When we get home, I tie the string of my balloon to my chair.

I have a bad dream in the night. I dream that my ears are sucking in every sound in the world, so many sounds I cannot breathe. I am choking with the sounds that are pulled into me, and I have to keep coughing the sounds away as they come in or I will smother.

"Here's some stuff for your cold," says my sister.

When I am awake again, I cannot tell if it is morning. I hear noises, but they are not the morning noises. My sister has her quiet voice, and I do not hear the little hard sounds of her heels making holes in the morning.

She is wearing slippers. She tells my mother she is not going to go to class today.

There is no hurry about today. I reach for my balloon. The string lies on the chair, and I find the balloon on the floor, small and soft and limp. It does not float. It lies in my hand, tired and sad.

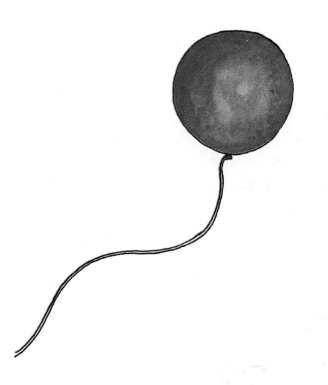

I lie there and listen to the sound of slippers on the kitchen floor.

I tap my good luck song against the wall over and over, but I hear the rain and know I will not go to the park today.

Tomorrow it will be a nice day. Tomorrow my sister will feel better, and I will go to the park and find Abram. He will make my balloon as good as new.

Now I walk over to the window and lean my head against it.

The rain taps its song to me against the glass, and I tap back.

Side Ways

A Boy's Best Friend

Isaac Asimov

Jimmy Anderson has a dog. Since Jimmy and his parents live in a Moon city, Jimmy's dog is not like the ones you have seen. Jimmy's dog, Robutt, is a robot. Will Jimmy take a real dog instead of Robutt? This story will tell you about the decision Jimmy had to make: Keep Robutt or have a REAL dog.

Mr. Anderson said, "Where is Jimmy, dear?"

"Out on the crater," said Mrs. Anderson. "He'll be all right. Robutt is with him. ——Did he arrive?"

"Yes. He's at the rocket station, going through the tests. Really, I can hardly wait to see him myself. I haven't seen one since I left Earth fifteen years ago. You can't count films."

"Jimmy has never seen one," said Mrs. Anderson.

"Because he's Moonborn and can't visit Earth. That's why I'm bringing one here. I think it's the first one ever on the Moon."

"It cost enough," said Mrs. Anderson, with a small sigh.

"Maintaining Robutt isn't cheap, either," said Mr. Anderson.

Jimmy was out on the crater, as his mother had said. By Earth standards, he was spindly, but rather tall for a ten-year-old. His arms and legs were long and agile. He looked thicker and stubbier with his space suit on, but he could handle the moon's gravity as no Earthborn human being could. His father couldn't begin to keep up with him when Jimmy stretched his legs and went into the kangaroo hop.

The outer side of the crater sloped to the south and the Earth, which was low in the southern sky (where it always was, as seen from Lunar City) was nearly full, so that the whole crater-slope was brightly lit.

The slope was a gentle one, and even the heavy space suit couldn't keep Jimmy from racing up it in a floating hop that made the gravity seem like nothing.

"Come on, Robutt," he shouted.

Robutt, who could hear him by radio, squeaked and bounced after.

Jimmy, expert though he was, couldn't outrace Robutt, who didn't need a space suit and had four legs and tendons of steel.

Robutt sailed over Jimmy's head, somersaulting and landing almost under his feet.

"Don't show off, Robutt," said Jimmy, "and stay in sight."

Robutt squeaked again, the special squeak that meant yes.

"I don't trust you, you faker," shouted Jimmy, and up he went in one last leap that carried him over the curved upper edge of the crater wall and down onto the inner slope.

The Earth sank below the top of the crater wall, and all at once it was pitch-dark around him. A warm, friendly darkness that wiped out the difference between ground and sky except for the shine of stars.

Actually, Jimmy wasn't supposed to play along the dark side of

the crater wall. The grown-ups said it was dangerous, but that was because they were never there. The ground was smooth and crunchy, and Jimmy knew the exact location of every one of the few rocks.

Besides, how could it be dangerous racing through the dark when Robutt was right there with him, bouncing around and squeaking and glowing? Even without the glow, Robutt could tell where he was, and where Jimmy was, by radar. Jimmy couldn't go wrong while Robutt was around. Robutt was always tripping him when he was too near a rock, or jumping on him to show how much he loved him, or circling around and squeaking low and scared when Jimmy hid behind a rock, when all the time Robutt knew well enough where he was. Once Jimmy had been very still and played like he was hurt. Robutt had sounded the radio alarm and people from Lunar City got there in a hurry. Jimmy's father had let him hear about that little trick. Jimmy never tried it again.

Just as he was remembering that, he heard his father's voice on his private wavelength. "Jimmy, come back. I have something to tell you."

Jimmy was out of his space suit now and washed up. You always had to wash up after coming in from outside. Even Robutt had to be washed, but he loved it. He stood there on all fours, his little foot-long body shaking and glowing just a tiny bit, and his small head, with no mouth, with two large glassed-in eyes, and with a bump where the brain was. He squeaked until Mr. Anderson said, "Quiet, Robutt."

Mr. Anderson was smiling. "We have something for you, Jimmy. It's at the rocket station now, but we'll have it tomorrow after all the tests are over. I thought I'd tell you now."

"From Earth, Dad?"

"A *dog* from Earth, son. A real dog. A Scotch terrier puppy. The first dog on the Moon. You won't need Robutt any more. We can't keep them both, you know, and some other boy or girl will have Robutt." He seemed to be waiting for Jimmy to say something; then he said, "You know what a dog is, Jimmy. It's the real thing. Robutt's only a mechanical imitation, a robot-mutt. That's how he got his name."

Jimmy frowned. "Robutt isn't an imitation, Dad. He's my dog."

"Not a real one, Jimmy. Robutt's just steel and wiring and a simple positronic brain. It's not alive."

"He does everything I want him to do, Dad. He understands me. Sure, he's alive."

"No, son, Robutt is just a machine. It's just programmed to act the way it does. A dog *is* alive. You won't want Robutt after you have the dog."

"The dog will need a space suit, won't he?"

"Yes, of course. But it will be worth the money, and he'll get used to it. And he won't need one in the City. You'll see the difference once he gets here."

Jimmy looked at Robutt, who was squeaking again, a very low, slow squeak that seemed frightened. Jimmy held out his arms, and Robutt was in them in one leap. Jimmy said, "What will the difference be between Robutt and the dog?"

"It's hard to explain," said Mr. Anderson, "but it will be easy to see. The dog will *really* love you. Robutt is just adjusted to act as though it loves you."

"But, Dad, we don't know what's inside the dog, or what his feelings are. Maybe it's just acting, too."

Mr. Anderson frowned. "Jimmy, you'll *know* the difference when you know the love of a living thing."

Jimmy held Robutt tightly. He was frowning, too, and the desperate look on his face meant that he wouldn't change his mind. He said, "But what's the difference how *they* act? How about how *I* feel? I love Robutt, and *that's* what counts."

And the little robot-mutt, which had never been held so tightly in all its existence, squeaked high and fast squeaks — happy squeaks.

Think About This:

1. What could a real dog do that Robutt could not?
2. Why did Jimmy's parents get a real dog for Jimmy?
3. Why did Jimmy want to keep Robutt?
4. Did Jimmy make the right decision? Why, or why not?

The Message

Raboo Rodgers

When Ben is trapped in an old mine shaft, he knows he could die. Ben must make a decision. He must decide whether to wait for the rescuers or to send them a signal. Decide for yourself whether you would make the same decision Ben makes.

It was a strange thing to have happen. More than that, it was an awful way to die.

Ben leaned back and poked at the pile of white bones with his toes. There were the skulls of three deer and two cattle. There were bones from smaller animals, too, but he wasn't sure about those.

He heard the helicopter again. This time he caught sight of it as it crossed the dot of light high over his head. He did not stand or wave or shout. He knew it would be useless.

Less than a hunded yards away, they were looking in the river for his body. The county rescue department would keep looking for him there.

Three days earlier, Ben and his friend Cody Burke had filled their air tanks and had gone diving for catfish. The water was muddy. The two divers had a hard time keeping each other in sight. Ben was behind Cody. Suddenly he saw a big cat. He held tightly to his steel catfish pole and followed it. The fish swam under a ledge and disappeared.

Ben went under the ledge and found himself in darkness. He took the small light from his belt and turned it on. Slowly he began kicking upward.

Ben broke through the surface of the water. He found himself in a small, damp cave.

On one side of the cave was a soft mud bank. Ben swam to it. He pulled himself from the water and flashed his light around the cave. Then he felt cold air.

The side of the cave where he stood was soft. There was a hole in it at knee level. Ben looked through the hole and saw another cave. He could see a dim light. It seemed far away. Ben dug at the hole with his hands. The soft, wet earth came away easily.

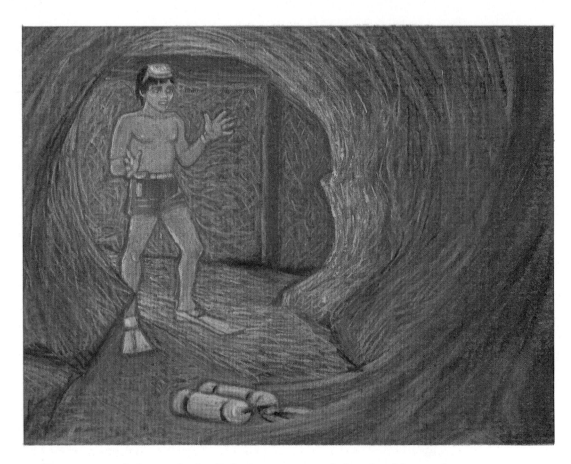

Ben stepped through the hole into a tunnel that had been dug there. It was held up by old timbers.

The tunnel sloped away from the river. Ben put down his air tank and walked quickly toward the light. When he reached it, he found that he had not come to the end of the tunnel. The tunnel rose there and broke through the ground far above. Ben knew where he was.

He was in an old empty mine shaft just yards away from the river. He had found a way to go into it under the water.

Ben turned and started back down the shaft toward the river.

A slurping noise made him think that something was wrong. When he reached the place where he had left his air tank, his fear turned to horror. Digging in the shaft, he had caused a mud flow.

Mud poured in from everywhere. He could not get back to the muddy pool. Ben was trapped! The only way out was up, but the opening was one hundred feet away.

He had yelled. He had beaten his steel pole against the air tank. Nothing helped.

At first, the helicopter searching the river excited him. But there was no way to signal it. After three days he had given up hope. He would die in here.

Looking at his air tank, he thought, "I've got a lot of air left. I used only a few minutes of it."

Ben had seen newspaper articles warning people about tanks that had blown up. An air tank could become a rocket if it blew up.

"Maybe I could blow up my tank somehow," Ben said, talking to himself. "Maybe they could hear it. Yeah, and maybe I'd bring this whole shaft down on me, too," he added. He played with the idea for a while. Then he got to his feet and went to work.

He took everything off the tank except the straps. He fastened the steel pole to the tank to guide it. Next, he attached one of his flippers to help steady the tank. Now the trick was to set it up.

Rocks covered the floor of the mine shaft. Ben chose a large one with a hard, sharp edge. He placed the tank valve down on the rock. Smaller rocks helped to prop it up.

Ben looked at what he had done. He had little hope that it would work. But it was the only chance he had. He checked the rocks around the tank, making sure that the tank rested on the valve.

As a last touch, Ben scratched a message on the side of the tank with his weight belt. It said: LOOK IN OLD MINE SHAFT.

Ben looked at more of the rocks on the floor of the shaft. He chose one that weighed about forty pounds and placed it near the tank. Then he waited.

He waited for a long time before he heard the helicopter come back. He picked up the rock and held it against his chest. The helicopter came closer. Ben lifted the rock above his head and held it.

"Now!" Ben thought. *"Now!"* With all his might he smashed the rock into the tank. The valve crashed against the hard rock. As if shot from a cannon, the tank took off.

Ben was on his back, looking up. The tank slammed into the side of the shaft and bounced off. The flipper and the steel pole kept the tank on course. Rocks and dirt rained down as the tank bounced from side to side. Then the tank shot toward the opening.

Ben was amazed. He watched the tank blast out into the sunlight and shoot high into the sky. Then it fell from sight.

Within fifteen minutes, heads appeared in the hole. One of the heads was Cody's. "Ben!" he shouted. "Ben!"

"You get my message, Cody?" Ben yelled up to him.

Cody laughed. "We got your message all right. I was in the helicopter. You nearly shot us out of the sky!"

The Great Spirit's Tower

Marion E. Gridley

Have you ever done something you were told not to do? If you have, then you have made the decision NOT to obey. Three young girls in this story did not obey. They decided to go away from their Indian camp after the chief told them to stay close by. This decision was not a good one, but the Great Spirit helped them.

Long ago a band of Indians wandered into a new country. They pitched their lodges close together in a camp circle. The chief told all the people to stay in sight of the tepees until the scouts could search the country and learn of its dangers.

It might be that wild beasts prowled over the plains around the camp. Unfriendly tribes might be near. And there might be many other unknown dangers.

Until the band of Indians could learn more about the country around them, they could not feel safe. So the scouts were sent out to hunt on the prairie, while the rest of the band stayed close to the camp.

But one day three young Indian girls wanted to go out onto the prairie to look for long grasses to use in making rugs. They asked if they could leave the camp.

"If you promise to be careful, you may go," the old chief told them. "But be sure to stay within sight of the camp circle."

The girls promised, and off they went. As they walked, they looked back now and then to see how far they were from the tepees.

But young people soon forget danger when their minds are filled with other things. The weather was sunny, and the country was beautiful. Flowers of bright colors grew all through the prairie grass. They were so lovely and their scent was so sweet that the

girls began to pick them. On and on they went, for always just ahead there was one brightly colored flower sweeter than all the rest. Each girl picked and picked until she had an armload of the tender flowers and long grasses.

The girls did not mean to disobey the word of their chief. But as they laughed and talked, they were so happy that they forgot what he had said. They wandered farther and farther from the camp. Soon the smoke from the campfire was a dim shadow in the distance.

From his home beyond the clouds the Great Spirit, who protected the Indians, watched the girls wander far out onto the prairie. He had heard the old chief tell them not to go far from camp, and he knew of the dangers in the land. He saw that although the girls did not know it, danger was close to them. Three grizzly bears had seen them. The bears, hidden in the tall grass, began to move quietly toward them.

When the girls were too far from camp to call for help, the grizzly bears leaped toward them, growling and showing their teeth. The girls ran, screaming. They could not decide which way to go!

The Great Spirit guided their feet to a large rock close by and helped them to its top. But even here they were not out of danger. The bears could climb, and they started up the sides of the rock. The girls could do nothing but stand close together in fear, watching the bears climb higher and higher.

The sides of the rock were smooth, and the bears dug their sharp claws into it to keep from falling. Sometimes they would slide back a little. But they climbed nearer and nearer.

Now the Great Spirit helped the young girls again. He knew they had not meant to disobey. They had only forgotten the chief's words, and the Great Spirit was sure they would not forget again.

So he spoke to the rock. As he spoke, the rock began to grow. Higher and higher it rose, with the bears still climbing up its sides. Their claws made deep scratches in the smooth surface as they tried to climb.

Up, up the rock went, until it was a great tower. Now the girls knew the Great Spirit was helping them, and they were no longer afraid. They watched the bears fight their way almost to the top of the rock. Then suddenly all three bears lost their hold and fell. They were so high when they fell that they were killed when they struck the ground.

The girls knelt and raised their arms toward the sky. They bowed their heads to show the Great Spirit that they were thankful for his help. Then they took the grass and flowers they had picked and twisted them into a long rope. Down this rope they swung to safety.

The girls ran back to camp and told the old chief what had happened. The chief did not scold them, for he knew they would never disobey again.

The Great Spirit did not change the rock, so it stayed as high as a tower. All along its sides were the deep scratches made by the grizzly bears. Whenever the Indians saw the magic tower, they lifted their faces to the sky and remembered that there beyond the clouds the Great Spirit was watching to protect them.

Think About This:

1. How do you think the Great Spirit felt when the bears leaped at the girls?
2. Why did the Great Spirit help the girls?
3. Should the chief have punished the girls? Why or why not?
4. What do you think the tower was? What in the story made you think that?

The Catfish That Walks

Val Thiessen

The walking catfish (Clarias batrachus) *was brought to southern Florida from Thailand. Tropical fish dealers sold the fish to
people who put them in fish ponds. Even though these catfish do
not grow over about eighteen inches long, they are causing problems for Florida. As you read this story, decide what you would do
to help Florida solve its problem with the walking catfish.*

Stories about strange animals have been told for hundreds of years. But few of these stories are true. They are more like dreams. A catfish that walks sounds very much like something out of a bad dream. But the walking catfish, Clarias batrachus, is a real fish, one of many that have come into Florida waters. Many of them have been sighted while walking on dry land. Can you imagine the surprise of someone seeing, for the first time, a fish walking on land? This walking fish has grown to be a real problem for Florida wild-life lovers.

Problems like that of the walking catfish come up again and again. In the last few years, a black fish has grown as rapidly as the walking catfish. The warm weather in Florida and the way ships can come in easily from far away make sure that other plants and animals will be introduced. Some of the new wild life may be like the horse, which was brought in from other lands. It became a great help to our country. So far, the walking catfish has been no help.

Clarias came from Thailand where it has been around for a long, long time. Florida is the home of many people who make their living by selling fish and animals. It seemed at first that these strange fish from Thailand would be interesting to American fish lovers. So some young fish, about two inches long, were ordered from their far-away home. When they came to Florida they sold well at first, but soon people tired of them. A large number was left in the shallow holding ponds of a fish dealer.

One night there were heavy rains, flooding the ponds. The walking catfish simply walked away. It can walk as far as a quarter of a mile. And the nearest open water was not nearly that far away.

In Florida, of course, there is a huge network of water, connected by canals, or separated by very small strips of land. Once out of the holding tanks, the walking catfish was free to invade the waters of Florida.

No one was certain that any real problem would occur. A few more fish in the millions that live in Florida waters seemed no real problem. But Clarias isn't just any fish.

For one thing, the walking catfish grows rapidly and reaches a large size. In Thailand, its home, it can reach twenty-two inches in length. In Florida, the longest has been eighteen inches.

Clarias, too, is a very fierce fish. It will attack and kill other large fish, even fish that many other fish would avoid. When a school of Clarias takes over a new pond, this is what happens.

In just a few weeks, all the eggs and small fish are killed out. Once the water life has been eaten, Clarias may go to sleep for a long time, until the next rainy night. Then it will try to walk over to the next pond, and repeat the whole thing in the pond next door.

And of course, you can't starve the walking catfish out. Clarias can go for several months without eating if it has to. And it will lose only a little weight.

Clarias, then, has no problem taking over Florida waters and killing other fish.

What is it like, this walking catfish, and how can it live out of water, and walk on land? A study of the fish gives some answers.

Surely no stranger fish or animal has ever lived. The walking catfish has a set of air-breathing lungs which lie just behind the gills. It has been seen coming up for air from the water after some eight minutes or so of water breathing.

Of course, Clarias is a fish, and likes being wet better than being dry. So if you want to see Clarias walk, the best time is during wet or rainy weather, and at night, when it is not so hot.

The first Clarias brought from Thailand were white to pinkish in color. But later some have changed to brown and grey colors like other native Florida fish. Clarias also has feelers, much like a cat's whiskers, that help it know about the world around it as our eyes and ears do for us. Like other catfish, Clarias can stick people who are not careful when they pick the fish up. Being stuck hurts enough so that you will remember it!

How far has the invasion of Florida's waters gone? So far only the center and the end of Florida have been taken over. But Clarias has reached one of the largest and most important lakes in the area. Many people fear for all the fish in that whole water system. One reason is that Clarias does not hold itself to eating just fish and fish eggs. It will eat worms, plants, insects — almost any life that can be found in the water around it.

No one can guess how much damage will finally be done if Clarias goes on with its invasion of many new lakes and ponds. Already people have tried to cut down on the numbers of the walking catfish. But reaching the decision to do this and then making it work are not the same thing. The decision was easy enough. When scientists looked at the fast increase in the numbers of Clarias, and the loss of other valuable fish, Clarias seemed more a bad fish than a good one. As food, it is thought to be worth eating, for scientists learned that in Thailand it is eaten by many people. But most Floridians do not like it nearly so well as the fish that it is killing. So its use as food is not worth letting it live.

A decision was made to kill out Clarias by poisoning the water. This had worked many times before with other kinds of fish that were no longer wanted. When the waters were poisoned, guess what the walking fish did! It just crawled out of the poisoned water, and walked until it reached clean water.

So how do you poison a fish that simply walks away when you put poison in its water? The answer is that you can't, but that you do poison the other fish who can't walk away. Poison was not the answer to the Clarias trouble.

Nature may give us an answer in time. Almost never have large numbers of new life moved in without being followed by other life that feeds on it. So there may be natural enemies to Clarias, who have not yet attacked it. One of the suggestions is that when Clarias reaches alligator country, the alligators may bring the fish under control. That may lead to another change — a lot more alligators. Or there may be some sickness that Clarias has not yet caught, a sickness that will kill Clarias more than it does other kinds of fish.

One thing is sure, that the natural enemy of most fish, dry weather, is not nearly so bad for Clarias. As the ponds and small water areas go dry, all other fish find themselves on dry land, where they die.Clarias, on the other hand, will simply leave the other fish to die, and walk to new water. While most of its walking is to find new food, it is also able to walk away from poison and dry holes. All in all, it's a very hard fish to kill.

In spite of this, Florida goes on trying to take care of the problem of too many walking catfish. A five-year study has been done, costing $125,000, with the hope that new knowledge of the walking catfish, gained both in the laboratory and in the open Florida waters, may well give us some ideas on how to stop the invasion.

One of the early findings of laboratory studies was learning that Clarias can not stand cold weather. This means that the fish will not walk too far north. When temperatures go below thirty degrees Fahrenheit for several days, some fish are killed. Others are weak and may die from sickness.

In time, of course, Clarias will get used to colder temperatures, and go into the states farther to the north. But for now, the fish will not walk and swim to cold states. By the time it is able to do this, scientists may have found the answer, a way to kill Clarias without killing every other form of life living nearby.

While we wait, if you are in Florida, you can see fish walking on dry land!

Think About This:

1. Why was the decision to bring the walking catfish to Florida a poor decision?
2. How is the walking catfish causing problems in Florida?
3. Would it be right to kill the walking catfish? Why or why not?
4. How would you help the state of Florida with its problem?

Catalogue

Rosalie Moore

Cats sleep fat and walk thin.
Cats, when they sleep, slump;
When they wake, stretch and begin
Over, pulling their ribs in.
Cats walk thin.

Cats wait in a lump,
Jump in a streak.
Cats, when they jump, are sleek
As a grape slipping its skin —
They have technique.
Oh, cats don't creak.
They sneak.

Cats sleep fat.
They spread out comfort underneath
   them
Like a good mat,
As if they picked the place
And then sat;
You walk around one
As if he were the city hall
After that.

If male,
A cat is apt to sing on a major scale;
This concert is for everybody, this
Is wholesale.
For a baton, he wields a tail.

(He is also found,
When happy, to resound
With an enclosed and private sound.)

A cat condenses.
He pulls in his tail to go under bridges,
And himself to go under fences.
Cats fit
In any size box or kit,
And if a large pumpkin grew under one,
He could arch over it.

When everyone else is just ready to go
    out,
The cat is just ready to come in.
He's not where he's been.
Cats sleep fat and walk thin.

City Hall

Nellie Burchardt

The poem you just read was about cats. The next story, "City Hall" is also about a cat and a decision Betsy and her friends make. They want to keep a cat. But keeping a pet would be breaking the Housing Project rules. Read to find out what decision Betsy and her friends make.

"Now let's all be real quiet," said Betsy when they got to City Hall. "They'll never let us see the mayor if we are noisy."

The children climbed the steps of the huge stone building. Down the long marble hall to the mayor's office they walked. The sound of their footsteps was lost in the great, high ceilings.

As they got to the mayor's office the other children held back more and more, leaving Betsy in front.

"Please, miss," she said to the lady at the desk by the door that said MAYOR, "we'd like to see the mayor."

"Do you have an appointment?" asked the lady, looking up from her typewriter.

"No. We didn't know you had to. But we have a petition for him."

The lady held out her hand. "I'll take care of it. You needn't wait," she said.

The children looked at each other. Ellen shook her head at Betsy but did not say anything.

"No," said Betsy. "We want to see the mayor in person."

"I'm sorry, but the mayor is very busy at a City Council meeting."

The children eyed each other again.

"We'll wait," said Betsy.

"I said the mayor is very busy," said the lady, beginning to sound annoyed. "You can't see him now."

"That's all right, miss. We have lots of time," said Betsy. "We'll sit down and wait till he's not busy." She turned and led the way to a bench against the wall. The other children followed her and sat down in a row on the bench.

The lady at the desk pushed back her chair and stood up. "Now, listen here, all of you," she said. "I told you that you *can't*

wait. The mayor is too busy to have a bunch of noisy kids hanging
around his office.''

The lady seemed quite angry. Betsy wished the other children
would not leave all the talking to her.

"We'll be very quiet, miss. Please — we just *have* to see him,"
she pleaded. "It's very urgent."

She stood up but stopped when she saw a door open behind the lady's back. A tall, rather stout man stood in the doorway. In the room behind him Betsy could see people walking around, talking to each other.

The lady did not see the man. She walked to the children with her arm raised, pointing at the door down the hall where they had come in.

"I said no! Now, out with you!" she said.

The man stepped forward.

"Come, come, Miss Witherspoon," he said, "that's no way to treat a group of future voters."

Miss Witherspoon spun around. "Oh — Mr. Mayor!" she gasped. "I didn't realize you were there. I'm so sorry if we disturbed you. I — I — I was just trying to get these children to leave, but they refuse to."

"Have you tried twisting their arms?" asked the mayor, with a wink at the children.

"Twisting their arms!" exclaimed Miss Witherspoon in a horrified voice. Then she giggled. "Oh — you're joking again. I just never know when you're joking."

"But I'm glad you didn't get them to leave," continued the mayor. "It's not every day that I get a chance to talk to a group of my younger constituents."

The children looked at each other.

"Now don't tell me that you didn't know you were my constituents," said the mayor.

The children shook their heads.

"Well, don't let it worry you. It just means you're the people I represent. You know what that means, don't you?"

The children nodded their heads.

"Now," said the mayor, "out with it. To what do I owe the honor of this visit?"

Ellen gave Betsy a shove, and Betsy had to take a step forward to keep from falling.

"Yes?" said the mayor.

When he looked at her, her stomach felt shaky. He had not seemed so big in the picture she had seen in the paper.

"We — we — we have a petition here for you, M-Mr. Mayor," said Betsy. She was surprised to hear how little and shaky her voice sounded. She handed him the papers covered with signatures.

The mayor took the papers from Betsy with one hand and with the other he reached into his pocket and pulled out his glasses. He put them on and read the petition, then turned the pages of signatures one by one and examined them carefully.

Finally he looked up at Betsy and said, "So I can have a pet and you can't, is that it?"

"Yes, sir," said Betsy in a tiny voice.

"And you don't think that's fair, eh?"

"N-n-no, sir."

"What kind of pet would you get if you could have one?"

Betsy took a deep breath. "A cat. You see, there's this poor little cat that has a hurt paw —"

Suddenly the other children found their voices and all started speaking at once.

"— and we've been feeding her —"

"— and she's going to have kittens —"

"— but we're not allowed to have pets —"

"— and the weather's getting too cold —"

"Whoa! Whoa!" shouted the mayor over the babble of voices. "One at a time!"

The children fell silent.

Now that he could make himself heard, the mayor looked right at Betsy and said, "This seems to be something of an emergency. Is that it?"

"Yes, sir," said Betsy. "She's going to have her kittens any day now. And Ellen's mother says if she has them outside she'll hide them somewhere and we won't be able to find them before winter comes."

"What do you say to that, Miss Witherspoon?" asked the mayor. "Kittens all over the place!"

Miss Witherspoon looked up from her desk, where she had gone back to her typing.

"Pardon me, sir?" she asked.

The mayor raised his voice. "I said we're going to have kittens all over the Project. Are we going to allow that?"

"Oh — no, sir," gasped Miss Witherspoon.

"You're right!" said the mayor. "Kittens all over the Project, scaring away the birds and digging up the flower beds. We certainly can't have that!"

Betsy's heart sank. Maybe they should not have come. And the mayor had seemed so nice at first.

"You know what I'd like to do?" the mayor asked.

"N-no, sir." Betsy's voice was small and scared.

"I'd *like* you children to take those kittens in and give them homes."

Betsy gave a sigh of relief. He was nice, after all!

"*But*," continued the mayor, "there's only one catch."

Betsy and her friends had worried looks.

"What's that?" asked Betsy.

"I don't make the rules. The City Council has to approve any change in the rules for the Project. You know, you're not the first ones to have said the rule against pets was not fair. Now — what could we do about it?"

The children watched his face.

"Hm-m-m — yes. It just might work," he said at last. He looked at Betsy. "What's your name, little girl?"

"Who? Me?" Betsy looked around, hoping he meant some other child.

"Yes — you."

"Oh. Betsy."

"All right, Betsy. Do you think you could go in there to the City Council meeting and show them the petition just the way you showed it to me?"

"Oh — no!" Betsy stepped back toward the protection of the rest of the group. "I'd be too scared."

"You weren't too scared of me, were you, Betsy?"

"No-o-o." She remembered she *had* been afraid of him. But that seemed a little silly now. He was not in the least bit mean or grumpy.

"Do you want to keep that cat, Betsy?" he asked.

"Oh — yes! I do!"

She bit her lip. That cat was making her do a lot of things she would have been too scared to do last year — talking back to Ellen, ringing all those strange doorbells to get signatures, talking to the mayor. And now he wanted her to face the City Council! Well, she'd come this far. She couldn't give it up now.

"All right. I *guess* I could do it," she said.

"That's the girl!" exclaimed the mayor.

As Betsy and the mayor entered the room, the council members went back to their seats. Betsy almost changed her mind when she saw all those strange grown-up faces looking at her from around the big council-room table. The council members looked like the kind of people who could say no to almost anything.

The mayor sat down in the chair at the head of the table and told her to stand beside him. He picked up a little wooden mallet and rapped on the table for quiet.

"I'd like to make a change in business," he said. "I want to

introduce a young lady to you. Her name is Betsy — uh — Betsy, what's your last name?"

"Delaney."

"Her name is Betsy Delaney, and she has a problem for you."

Betsy felt a little braver. She tried not to think of all those grown-up eyes looking at her. She tried to think instead of the cat's green-and-gold eyes.

Once she started talking, it was not as hard as she had thought it would be to tell about the petition and the lame cat the children had been feeding. When she had finished and had passed around the petition for all of them to look at, the mayor whispered in her ear, "This isn't a promise, Betsy, but if I were you, I'd go home and catch that cat and lock her up before she starts having kittens all over the place."

Betsy grinned. "Oh, yes, sir!" she said.

As she turned to leave, she saw the mayor wink at her. She winked back. It seemed silly now that she had been so scared of him at first.

I'm as bad as the cat, she thought. I get scared of things before I know if there's really anything to be scared of.

She was not sure, but she thought that two of the council members were smiling. She was not quite brave enough yet to look right at all those strange grown-up faces. But she *had* gotten them to look at the petition. That was the main thing.

Think About This:

1. Did the mayor and city council members change the no-pets rule? Why or why not?
2. What other way could Betsy and her friends have tried to change the no-pets rule?
3. What important decisions have you had to make?

It's Up to You

Jill Irving

Advertisements are all around you. A football player tries to sell you a bicycle or bubble gum. Race-car drivers try to sell you hot dogs or tennis shoes. Someone always seems to be trying to sell you something.

Look for advertisements. Magazines, cereal boxes, road signs, comic books, TV, store windows, and newspapers all have them. Advertisements can tell you all about something. Then you can decide if you want to buy it. Advertisements can make a product look very good. They may even make you feel that you MUST buy.

Look at the following advertisement. While you are reading, think about what the words make you feel. Think about what the author is trying to get you to do.

> "*Step right up, ladies and gentlemen. I have here the one and only real snake oil,* Pretty Skin. *It is the greatest beauty aid ever known. It makes the skin soft and healthy, and gives it a pleasant glow. What more do you expect an oil to do? Come up here, young person! Have you ever tried* Pretty Skin? *You have? Did it do what I said? Yes? Wonderful! What's that, sir? Will it cure warts? Of course it will. How do I know?* Pretty Skin *does everything. So step right up and buy the world's greatest beauty aid,* Pretty Skin. *Why? Because everybody is! It's a low, low price, today only.*"

You may never have seen an advertisement as silly as this one about *Pretty Skin*. But this shows you some things about advertising. Does *Pretty Skin* give any proof that it will do what it says? Does it tell you what *Pretty Skin* is made of? Would all the things that make up *Pretty Skin* be good for you? After reading about *Pretty Skin*, would you buy it?

For food, look at the cover or lid of the box, can, or jar. There is a law which says that anything to eat or drink must be labeled to show what it is made of. Look before you buy. If you are not sure what the names of the ingredients mean, try to find out. How? Look in a dictionary. Ask your teacher or your parents. Or check with a drugstore. Some companies put their addresses on their packaging. You can write to the company and ask them to tell you just what their goods are made of.

Whether or not you buy advertised goods is up to you. The

advertisements that follow are for several different kinds of products. Study them carefully. Think about what each one says. Why do you buy an advertised product? Think about your own needs. Which of the following would you buy? It's up to you.

SIDEWALK SURFER...
THE SMOOTH-SAILING SKATEBOARD FOR THE
REAL PRO!

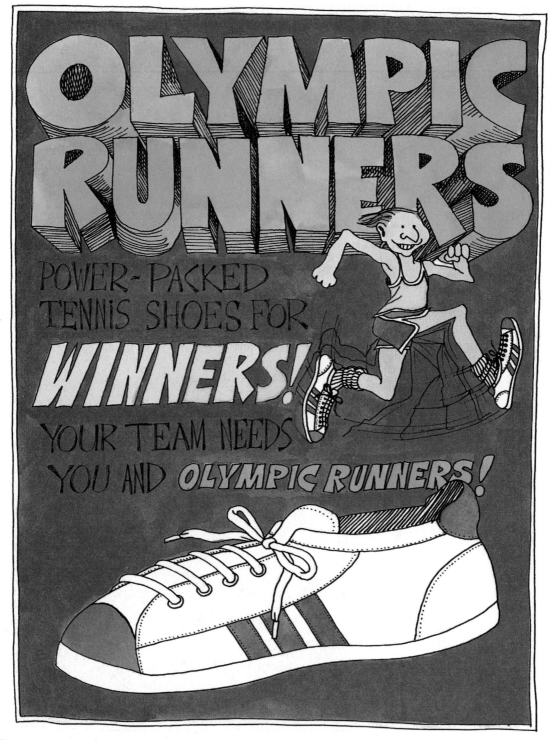

Think About This:

1. What are some ways to find out about a product?
2. Which advertisements most made you want to buy the products? Why?
3. Where are some other places you have seen advertisements?

Inside Out

Signatures

Your signature is your name, your own way of telling everyone that you are you. And every person's signature is different. Here are four different kinds of signatures.

Clowns are always easy to identify by their colorful make-up and costumes. But did you know that each clown always wears the same face, and that no two faces are ever exactly alike? Look at these clowns. Each of their faces is different, since the make-up of each clown is that clown's personal signature.

Truck drivers identify themselves on their CB radios by names which they make up. These names are called "handles." Many times a handle tells something about the person using it. These handles suggest pictures.

Sad Sack

Mean Man

King Cobra

Rug Head

Bush Whacker

War Eagle

Handwriting changes from person to person. Everyone forms letters differently and joins them together in different ways. People can be identified by the way in which they form their letters, slant their letters, and join them together.

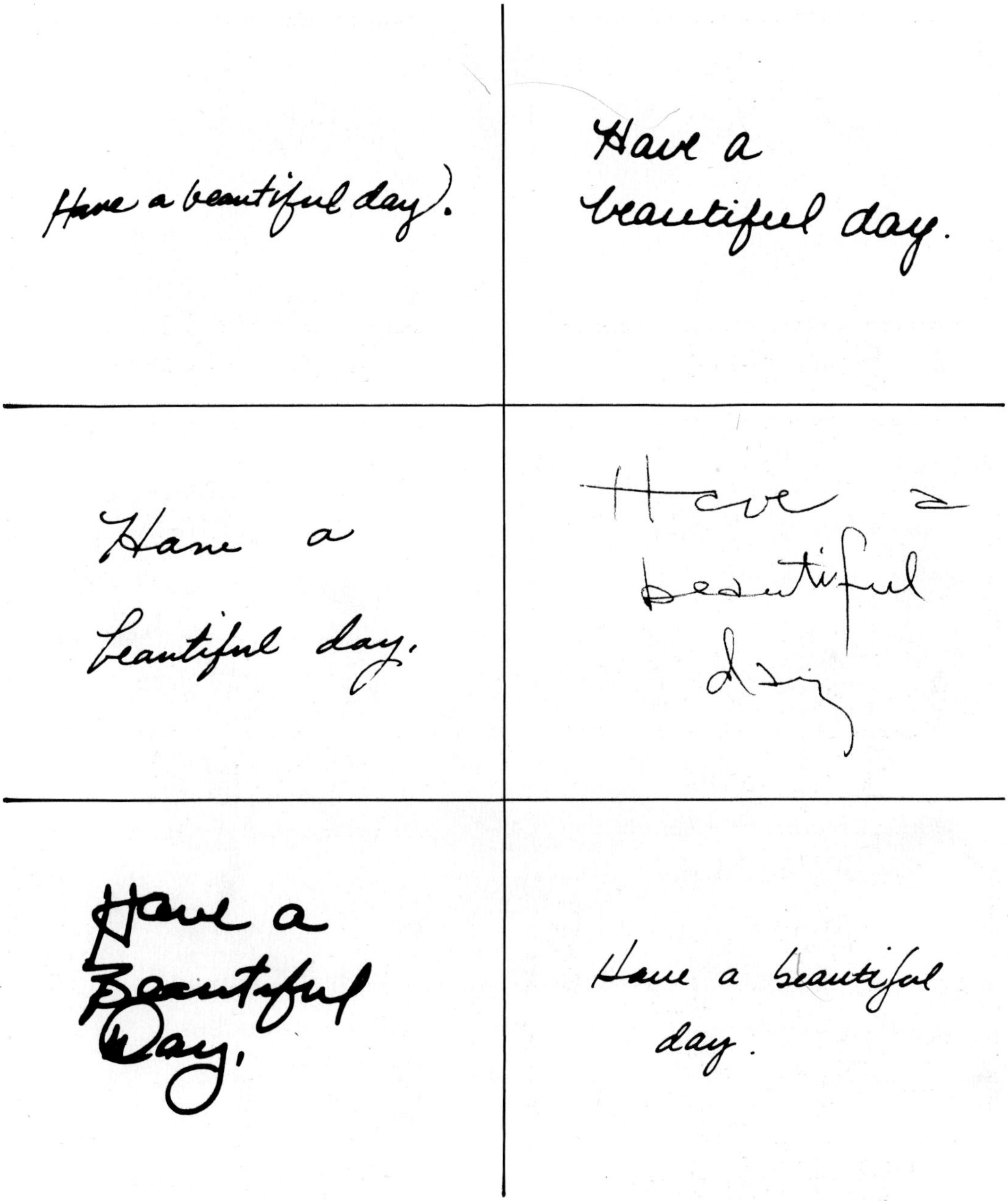

Have a beautiful day).

Have a beautiful day.

Have a beautiful day.

Have a beautiful day

Have a Beautiful Day.

Have a beautiful day.

The ancient Egyptians used marks with ovals drawn around them for their signatures. These signatures are called cartouches. Inside the oval shape of the cartouche are symbols which give a picture of the person. These pictures inside the oval shape are called hieroglyphs.

This is the personal cartouche of Tutankhamun before he became king of all of Egypt. The pictures mean "Tutankhamun, ruler of On of Upper Egypt."

This is Tutankhamun's royal cartouche after he became king of all of Egypt. His royal name became "Nebkheperura." The scarab, or beetle, is underneath a circle, which stands for the sun. The scarab stood for the sun god in ancient Egypt. These hiero-glyphs were fitting for a king's royal cartouche.

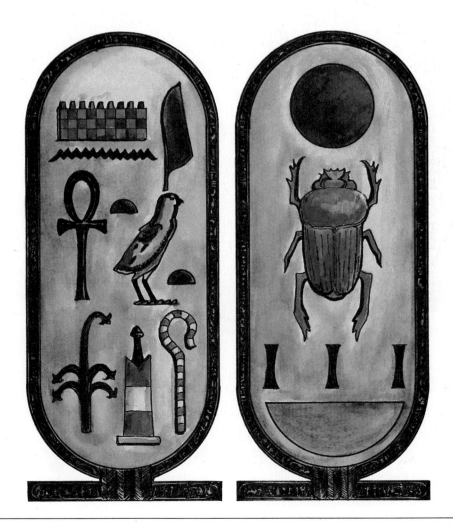

Harriet the Spy ———————

Louise Fitzhugh

 Harriet plans to be a famous writer. She practices all the time by filling secret notebooks with comments about the people she knows. But what would happen if her friends should read her special notebooks? Harriet finds out one day, and suddenly she is faced with a real problem. What will happen when Harriet's special secret is out in the open?

That day, after school, everyone felt in a good mood because the weather was suddenly gay and soft like spring. They hung around outside, the whole class together, which was something they never did. Sport said suddenly, "Hey, why don't we go to the park and play tag?"

Harriet was late for her spying, but she thought she would just play one game and then leave. They all seemed to think this was a smashing idea, so everyone filed across the street.

The kind of tag they played wasn't very complicated; in fact, Harriet thought it was rather silly. The object seemed to be to run around in circles and get very tired, then whoever was "it" tried to knock everyone else's books out of their arms. They played and played. Beth Ellen was eliminated at once, having no strength. Sport was the best. He managed to knock down everyone's books except Rachel Hennessey's and Harriet's.

He ran round and round then, very fast. Suddenly he knocked a few of Harriet's things off her arms, then Rachel tried to tease him away, and Harriet started to run like crazy. Soon she was running and running as fast as she could in the direction of the mayor's house. Rachel was right after her and Sport was close behind.

They ran and ran along the river. Then they were on the grass and Sport fell down. It wasn't any fun with him not chasing, so Rachel and Harriet waited until he got up. Then he was very quick and got them.

All of Rachel's books were on the ground, and some of Harriet's. They began to pick them up to go back and join the others.

Suddenly Harriet screeched in horror, "Where is my notebook?" They all began looking around, but they couldn't find it anywhere. Harriet suddenly remembered that some things had been knocked down before they ran away from the others. She began to run back toward them. She ran and ran, yelling like a banshee the whole way.

When she got back to where they had started, she saw the whole class — Beth Ellen, Pinky Whitehead, Carrie Andrews, Marion Hawthorne, Laura Peters, and The Boy with the Purple Socks — all sitting around a bench while Janie Gibbs read to them from the notebook.

Harriet descended upon them with a scream that was supposed to frighten Janie so much she would drop the book. But Janie didn't frighten easily. She just stopped reading and looked up calmly. The others looked up too. She looked at all their eyes and suddenly Harriet M. Welsch was afraid.

They just looked and looked, and their eyes were the meanest eyes she had ever seen. They formed a little knot and wouldn't let her near them. Rachel and Sport came up then. Marion Hawthorne said fiercely, "Rachel, come over here." Rachel walked over to her, and after Marion whispered in her ear, got the same mean look.

Janie said, "Sport, come over here."

"Whadaya mean?" said Sport.

"I have something to tell you," Janie said in a very pointed way.

Sport walked over and Harriet's heart went into her sneakers. "FINKS!" Harriet felt rather hysterical. She didn't know what the word meant, but since her father said it all the time, she knew it was bad.

Janie passed the notebook to Sport and Rachel, never taking her eyes off Harriet as she did so. "Sport, you're on page thirty-four; Rachel, you're on fifteen," she said quietly.

Sport read his and burst into tears. "Read it aloud, Sport," said Janie harshly.

"I can't," Sport hid his face.

The book was passed back to Janie. Janie read the passage in a solemn voice.

SOMETIMES I CAN'T STAND SPORT. WITH HIS WORRYING ALL THE TIME AND FUSSING OVER HIS FATHER, SOMETIMES HE'S LIKE A LITTLE OLD WOMAN.

Sport turned his back on Harriet, but even from his back Harriet could see that he was crying.

"That's not *fair*," she screamed. "There's some nice things about Sport in there."

Everyone got very still. Janie spoke very quietly. "Harriet, go over there on that bench until we decide what we're going to do to you."

Harriet went over and sat down. She couldn't hear them. They began to discuss something rapidly with many gestures. Sport kept his back turned and Janie never took her eyes off Harriet, no matter who was talking.

Harriet thought suddenly, I don't have to sit here. And she got up and marched off in as dignified a way as possible under the circumstances. They were so busy they didn't even seem to notice her.

At home, eating her cake and milk, Harriet reviewed her position. It was terrible. She decided that she had never been in a worse position. She then decided she wasn't going to think about it any more. She went to bed in the middle of the afternoon and didn't get up until the next morning.

Her mother thought she was sick and said to her father, "Maybe we ought to call the doctor."

"Finks, all of them," said her father. Then they went away and Harriet went to sleep.

In the park all the children sat around and read things aloud. These are some of the things they read:

NOTES ON WHAT CARRIE ANDREWS THINKS OF MARION HAWTHORNE

THINKS: IS MEAN
            IS ROTTEN IN MATH
            HAS FUNNY KNEES
            IS A PIG

Then:

IF MARION HAWTHORNE DOESN'T WATCH OUT SHE'S
GOING TO GROW UP INTO A LADY HITLER.

Janie Gibbs smothered a laugh at that one but not at the next
one:

WHO DOES JANIE GIBBS THINK SHE'S KIDDING? DOES
SHE REALLY THINK SHE COULD EVER BE A SCIENTIST?

Janie looked as though she had been struck. Sport looked at
her sympathetically. They looked at each other, in fact, in a long,
meaningful way.

....

Harriet looked around and, seeing no one, climbed over the
iron railing in front of this alley. A cat with one eye stared at her.
She landed with a thump and the cat with one eye hissed, backing
away.

She ran to the back of the alley, her tools jangling. She climbed the fence and from there could see the whole stretch of the block of gardens. Rachel's was the fourth one over. Hoping that no one in the buildings would see her, or if they did they would keep their mouths shut, she began to climb fences and run through gardens

until she came to the fence right next to Rachel's garden. Through a crack she could see and hear almost everything. She heard their voices, excited and screeching at each other, and saw a big piece of lumber rise up.

"Listen, Pinky, you're just stupid. This piece should go here, not over there." This was clearly Carrie Andrews talking.

Then Harriet saw the flagpole. It was a rather short flagpole, but it was a real one. At the top of it, fluttering against the blue sky, was a pair of purple socks.

Harriet stared at the socks. A dim feeling began to penetrate her. She didn't know what the feeling was until her heart began to beat fast, then she knew it was fear. Those socks made her afraid. If she could see what they were doing, maybe she wouldn't be afraid anymore.

"YOU'RE AN IDIOT!" Carrie Andrews said to Pinky Whitehead.

"How can I build anything without a level?" Sport said to everyone in general.

Then Harriet found a hole and looked through. They were building a *house!* Incredible. But there they were. Everyone was rushing around with tools and wood and there was the semblance of a house emerging right in front of her. It leaned, of course. In fact the two back walls were the corner of the fence and it appeared to be pulling the fence down; but, never mind, it was a house.

Sport was in charge. He was telling everyone what to do in a very irritated way. Carrie Andrews seemed to be the second in command. Except for about three pieces of new wood, the rest was old rotten wood from a chest they had broken up. The three new pieces didn't seem to bear any relation to each other. There were a couple of chairs being chopped up by Pinky right at that moment. Harriet scrunched closer to the fence to see better.

It was a funny scene. Carrie Andrews stood over Sport, yelling at the top of her lungs even though her mouth was right next to his ear. Sport was hammering a floor together. Laura Peters, Marion Hawthorne, and Rachel Hennessey were running around like fools. They had no idea how to do anything. Rachel tried to hammer and smashed her finger. After a while they got bored with trying and got into a conversation near Harriet's post. Janie joined them after an upright fell on her head.

"She's going to die when she finds out."

"Serves her right, mean thing."

"Boy, will she be jealous."

"She has delusions of grandeur anyway," said Janie, rubbing her head.

Harriet was puzzled. Who? Who were they talking about? She looked over and saw Beth Ellen in a corner by herself. What was she doing? She appeared to be drawing something on an old piece of wood. That was the one thing Beth Ellen could do, draw. But then Harriet looked more closely and saw that she wasn't exactly drawing, she was making letters on a sign in a very painstaking way.

Just at that moment the back door opened and Mrs. Hennessey called out, "Okay, kids, the cake is ready. Come and get it."

Homemade cake. Of course. That's why they had chosen Rachel's garden. Not everyone had a garden, but Janie did, and Beth Ellen did. Beth Ellen probably wouldn't even give you an olive to eat over there. Once Harriet had spent the afternoon there and just to pass the time had looked in the refrigerator. There hadn't been anything but a jar of mayonnaise, a jar of artichoke hearts in olive oil, and some skimmed milk. Beth Ellen had agreed

with her that it wasn't enough and had added that she felt hungry all the time because her nurse was on a diet and her grandmother was always out to dinner.

There was a mad scramble on the other side of the fence as they all ran to the back door and piled inside. Harriet felt lonely and rather hungry. She stood a minute thinking, then she went back through the gardens the way she had come.

Think About This:

1. Why was Harriet so upset when she discovered that her notebook was missing?
2. Why did Harriet feel lonely when the children went inside for cake?
3. Why did Harriet keep a notebook?
4. What can Harriet do about the problems her notebook created?

Muscles Make You Move

Edith Lucie Weart

Each person has a special signature and special feelings. And each person is a little different from everyone else. But everyone has a body with muscles. Muscles let people move. Muscles let people walk, run, and play sports. How do those muscles work? It's a wonderful story.

You walk up and down stairs. You reach down to pick up a ball and throw it. You bite into an apple, run for a bus, write a letter. You can do all these things without any trouble at all, without really thinking about it.

Yet all these moves are different. None would be possible without bones and the muscles which are joined to them.

All the bones together make up the skeleton of the body. Connected to the bones are the skeletal muscles.

These are the muscles which make it possible to walk, throw a ball, and do all the thousand and one things which make use of motion.

Muscles make up almost half of what the body weighs. Muscles are of many different sizes. There is one in the middle ear which is only a very tiny part of an inch long. On the other hand, the calf of the leg is almost nothing but muscle.

Working with the muscles are tendons which join them to the bones.

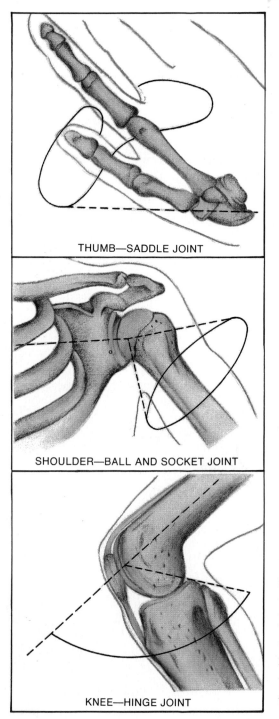

THUMB—SADDLE JOINT

SHOULDER—BALL AND SOCKET JOINT

KNEE—HINGE JOINT

These are very strong cords. You can see them very well on the back of the fingers. When you make a fist, you can see them move. Also working with the bones, helping to hold them together where they join, are other strong bands called ligaments.

Joints are the places in the body where two bones come together. They make it possible to move.

There are several different kinds.

A *hinge* works like a door which moves in only one direction. Can you name one? Stop to think a moment. Here are two: the elbow, and the knee.

There is also the *ball and socket*, where one end of the bone can roll around in the hollowed-out space of the bone it fits into. Where the bones join at the shoulder, the head of the bone in the arm is rounded and fits into the shoulder bone. Move your shoulder. You can feel the ball and socket move. You can move the shoulder in any direction.

A *saddle* allows even more freedom to move. The base of the thumb is a case in point. The fact that the thumb can move freely has greatly helped people to deal with the world around them. It has made it possible for the hand to hold and use tools and weapons — to make and use large things and very small things. Some-

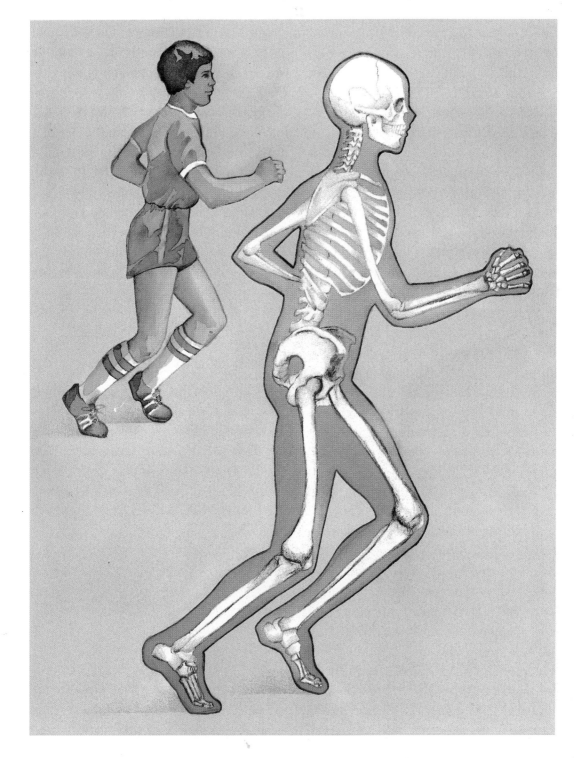

time tie your thumb so it can't move. You will quickly find that you can't do many things which are easy when you use your thumb.

Muscles often work in pairs. When one must become shorter to move a joint, another has to stretch out longer to allow the move. This is easy to see in moving the fingers to make a fist. The muscles which move the tendons on the inside of the fingers are now short, the ones which move those on the outside, long.

The way muscles move can also be seen in the upper arm. When the fist is closed hard and the elbow bent, those on the inside of the upper arm stand out.

A very large number of moves are made possible by the different ways the muscles and tendons move the bones. The bones are the frame for movement.

Even though you run, jump, and take your bones and muscles through many different acts, you do this without thinking about what you are doing. You don't tell each muscle just how it should move. As a matter of fact, you slowly build up this skill over a very long time, starting from the day you are born. A baby is about five months old before it is able to hold a toy tightly. The baby tries and fails and tries again. The brain sends orders through the nerves to the muscles. When they finally do what the brain tells them, a pattern is set up. Each time the baby holds a toy, the muscles are surer of the lesson learned. The same is true of every move the body makes. After a while, no time passes between the thought and the act. At least, the time is so short it can hardly be measured.

How the brain and nerves work is another story. Everything about the way the body works is a wonderful tale.

Think About This:

1. What are the different kinds of joints in the body?
2. How do muscles work in pairs?
3. With what other activities, besides those mentioned in the article, do you need muscles in order to perform?

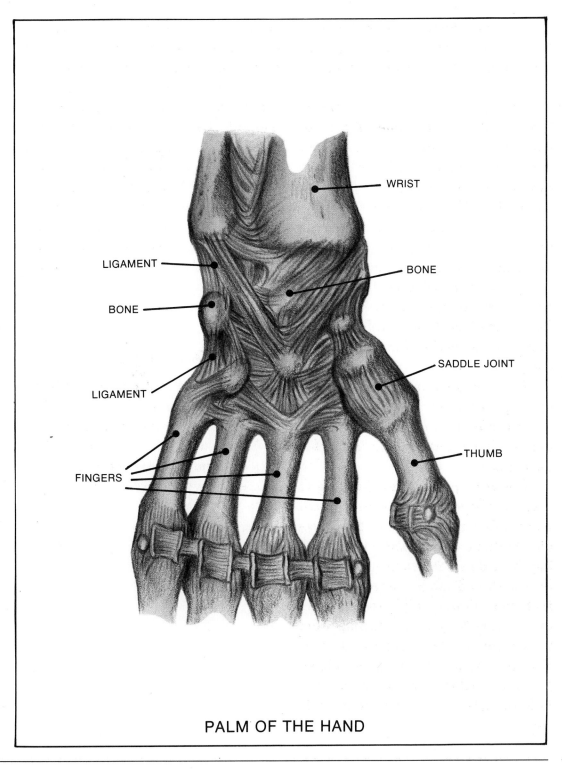

WRIST

LIGAMENT

BONE

BONE

SADDLE JOINT

LIGAMENT

THUMB

FINGERS

PALM OF THE HAND

Inside Me and Outside Me

There are many elements that join together to make every person special. The two poems that follow talk about two ways of looking at someone—inside and outside. The self-portraits by some famous artists show how they see themselves.

Phizzog

This face you got,
This here phizzog you carry around,
You never picked it out for yourself,
 at all, at all — did you?
This here phizzog — somebody handed it
 to you — am I right?
Somebody said, "Here's yours, now go see
 what you can do with it."
Somebody slipped it to you and it was like
 a package marked:
"No goods exchanged after being taken away" —
This face you got.

Carl Sandburg

maggie and milly and molly and may

maggic and milly and molly and may
went down to the beach(to play one day)

and maggie discovered a shell that sang
so sweetly she couldn't remember her troubles,and

milly befriended a stranded star
whose rays five languid fingers were;

and molly was chased by a horrible thing
which raced sideways while blowing bubbles:and

may came home with a smooth round stone
as small as a world and as large as alone.

For whatever we lose(like a you or a me)
it's always ourselves we find in the sea

e. e. cummings

Triple Self-Portrait, Norman Rockwell

Reprinted from *The Saturday Evening Post* © 1960   The Curtis Publishing Company

Self-Portrait, 1934, Malvin Grey Johnson

Self-Portrait, Suzanne Valadon

Think About This:

1. What is a "phizzog"?
2. What did "maggie and milly and molly and may" learn about themselves at the sea?
3. What would you draw in your own self-portrait?
4. How would you describe each of the people shown in the illustrations?

Grand Papa and Ellen Aroon

F. N. Monjo

Grand Papa is not only Ellen Aroon's grandfather. He is also the president of a new country, the United States. Grand Papa is a president who has many friends, and also some enemies. One group of enemies, "the Feds," call Grand Papa "Mr. Mammoth." That is because he collects old bones of big dinosaurs and other mammoth prehistoric animals. Although Ellen never says so in the story, she and Grand Papa have some very special feelings for each other. In this story, Ellen tells a lot about the United States, about Thomas Jefferson, and about herself.

In Washington City

Washington City is just a tiny town. Grand Papa says there aren't but 3,210 people living there. The streets are muddy. Grand Papa had some poplar trees planted along Pennsylvania Avenue, but they're still just tiny.

Only part of the Capitol is finished. And the President's House isn't finished either. Some of the rooms don't have any plaster on the ceilings. Mama says it's a big drafty barn.

Grand Papa says it's big enough for "two emperors, one pope, and the grand lama in the bargain." There aren't any stone steps up to the front door yet. You have to walk up a wooden ramp to get to the entrance hall.

Grand Papa and Papa were mighty glad to see Mama and all of us children. Grand Papa has a steward here who's French, named Etienne Lemaire. He lets us have pancakes for breakfast. Guess how he spells pancakes? *Panne-quaques*! (That's because he's French!)

Sometimes Grand Papa has to have big dinners at night for the ambassadors from England and France and Spain.

Jeff says one night, when Grand Papa had a big dinner, the Dutch Ambassador was there. Everybody helped themselves to a spoonful of sticky white pudding. Then the Dutch Ambassador dropped his napkin. When he leaned down to pick it up, by accident, his chin whiskers went into the pudding on his plate! Jeff heard the poor man whisper, "I vish I vass dead!" (I reckon he was embarrassed!)

You know who Grand Papa hates? Napoleon. He's the emperor of the French. Grand Papa says Napoleon wants to rule the whole world. Grand Papa calls Napoleon "a most determined villain."

Mama says Napoleon used to own a great big chunk of land,

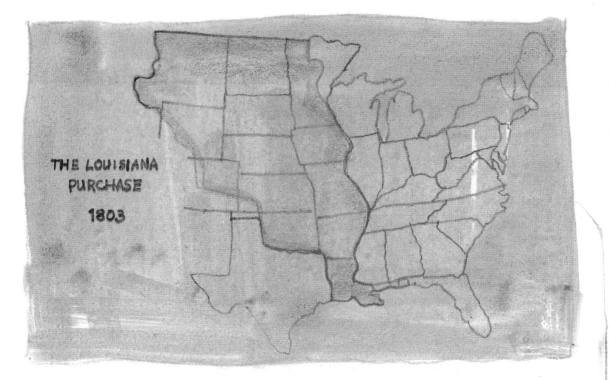

THE LOUISIANA PURCHASE 1803

called Louisiana, right next to our country. But three years ago, Mama says, Grand Papa started trying to buy the whole parcel. So he sent a friend of his — Mr. James Monroe — over to France to talk to Napoleon.

When Mr. Monroe bought it for him, Grand Papa *doubled* the size of our country! And he didn't need any extra taxes to do it. And he didn't go to war for it, either!

Mama made me figure out in an arithmetic lesson. Here's how much Grand Papa had to pay for Louisiana: $15,000,000. And here's what he got for the money: 1,171,931 square miles of land. Mama says that Louisiana cost Grand Papa about $12.80 per square mile. She says that's quite a good bargain! Of course Grand Papa is still just *guessing* at how much land is out there. Nobody knows for sure. Nobody knows how far it stretches, or just who lives there.

Grand Papa says there may be wooly mammoths or even

dinosaurs still living out there! He says somewhere in it, it may have a huge mountain of salt!

The Feds laugh at Grand Papa. They say, "Isn't that just like Mr. Mammoth? Next thing he'll be telling us there's a valley full of corn pudding way up the Missouri River! And a great big lake of molasses!"

But Grand Papa doesn't care how much the Feds laugh at him. He's sent Meriwether Lewis (who used to be his private secretary) and William Clark, and some soldiers and trappers out there to see what they can see. He wants them to go all the way up the Missouri River, and clear on out to the Pacific Ocean, if they can!

I've gotten to know Mrs. Dolley Madison. Dolley Madison is married to short, little old James Madison. Mr. Madison is one of Grand Papa's best friends. He's Grand Papa's Secretary of State, and helps him run things in Washington City.

Dolley Madison told me how it was when Grand Papa first came in, as President, way back on March 4, 1801. She told me about the parade they had, in Philadelphia, for Grand Papa. There were only sixteen states then. Now there are seventeen. In the parade there were sixteen white horses hitched to a carriage. One horse for every state of the Union. And set on top of the carriage was a big ship of state with sails set and flags flying. It was called the *Thomas Jefferson*. And people shot off cannons and cheered.

And Dolley Madison told me how all kinds of Indian chiefs come here to talk to Grand Papa when he has his Galas on the Fourth of July and on New Year's Day. A Gala is a big party. Grand Papa won't have any parties any other time *but* New Year's Day and the Fourth of July.

Grand Papa told me that one year some farmers from Massachusetts made him a present of a great big enormous cheese. It

was four feet wide, and it weighed 1,235 pounds. That's more than half a ton! But Grand Papa wouldn't take it as a gift. He paid the men $200 for it. Grand Papa doesn't believe in taking presents while he's President.

Yesterday Grand Papa let me eat a new dessert made by his French cook. Nobody in this country has ever tasted it before. It's called ice cream.

And now I have to tell you about Dick. Dick is Grand Papa's pet mockingbird. Grand Papa keeps him in a cage in his study. Lots of times he lets Dick out of his cage. Dick sits on Grand Papa's shoulder. He flies around from chair to chair. Grand Papa loves mockingbirds. I don't know what he'd do without Dick. Grand Papa once told me and Sister Anne and Jeff and Cornelia and Virginia and Mary that if we *ever* harmed a mockingbird, or stole eggs from its nest, the mockingbirds would come back and haunt us! And Mama says it's true!

At Monticello

We're all back home at Edgehill. Even Papa is here. Papa's full name is Thomas Mann Randolph. He's part Indian. He has dark hair. He's descended from Pocahontas.

Later on this summer Grand Papa will come to Virginia, too. Here's the first thing Grand Papa does when he comes to Edgehill. He carries every single one of us over to *his* house, Monticello, to be with him all summer long; Mama and Papa, Sister Anne and Jeff, Cornelia, Virginia, Mary, baby James Madison, and me, Ellen Aroon! Grand Papa wants all of us with him, Uncle Jack Eppes and Francis and Maria, and all of our aunts and uncles and cousins. He wants his whole family to be with him at Monticello.

You can see Monticello from Edgehill. It's way up on top of a mountain, about four or five miles away. Grand Papa says its name means "Little Mountain" in Italian. Grand Papa named it, and found the mountain he wanted to build it on, and drew the plans for the house all by himself.

Mama says Grand Papa is a fine architect. There's no other house quite like it in Virginia, or in the whole world. From way up there, you can look in every direction for miles and miles. Most people want their houses to look bigger than they really are, but Grand Papa designed Monticello to look *smaller* than it really is.

Monticello really has three stories, but Grand Papa designed it to look as if it hadn't got but one! Isn't that *just* like Grand Papa? He thinks Monticello is the loveliest spot on earth. So does Mama. And so do I.

Grand Papa orders plants and shrubs and trees from all over the world for his hilltop. They come from France and Italy and China and Spain. He has every kind of tree you can think of: flowering trees, shade trees, evergreen trees, nut trees, fruit trees. He grows walnuts and pecans, chestnuts, hickory nuts, and butternuts, apples, pears, and strawberries, and grapes and plums, raspberries and currants, persimmons and figs, and peaches, watermelons, and nectarines. His gardeners, Wormley and Goliath, grow celery and radishes, asparagus and lettuce, cauliflower and onions, carrots and beets, corn and squash, broccoli, spinach, and beans. And they grow Grand Papa's favorite vegetable, green peas.

I quit counting how many different kinds of peas there were, after I counted nineteen! Peas are one of the first vegetables to get ripe for the table in spring. Do you know what Grand Papa does when his very first mess of garden peas are ready to eat in the springtime? He asks all his neighbors to come to dinner, to help him celebrate.

One time, when the peas came in, Grand Papa asked Mr. and Mrs. Madison to come to dinner. Mr. Madison likes to lean back in his chair at the table, and he was sitting in front of an open window that goes right down to the floor. Mr. Madison likes to imitate politicians. He was imitating Patrick Henry.

"Here's what Patrick Henry says about Mr. Jefferson," said Mr. Madison. "He says Mr. Jefferson eats so much fine French cooking, he's quit eating all his favorite Virginia foods. No more ham! No more cornbread! He has abjured his native vittles!" And

Mr. Madison commenced laughing so hard, he fell backwards, right out of the window onto the lawn!

The next day, Grand Papa told Heming, the carpenter, to put railings on all those windows.

Then there's Uncle Isaac. He works at Monticello. Uncle Isaac remembers the Revolution. He told me about the time — when he was just a little boy about seven — when the British cavalry rode up the mountain to Monticello, trying to capture Grand Papa. Grand Papa knew they were coming, so he could ride away in plenty of time. But Isaac stayed behind, here, to help bury the silverware under the porch. The British never got hold of it.

Do you know why the British wanted to catch Grand Papa? They were angry with him. It was because of a letter he wrote to their king, King George III. Mama says *he* was a tyrant, too! What Grand Papa wrote was not a letter, really. It was more like an *announcement*. What Grand Papa wrote in it was that from now on everybody in America was going to be free. It was called the Declaration of Independence. Grand Papa showed me the little writing desk he wrote it on. He had the desk made in Philadelphia. It's in his library.

Mama says Grand Papa finished writing the Declaration of Independence on July 4, 1776. Mama says that's why we have barbecue and fireworks every year on this day. If it wasn't for Grand Papa, we wouldn't have any reason at all to celebrate the Fourth of July!

Mama got a letter from Grand Papa today. Guess what happened? He's heard from Lewis and Clark — the men he sent out to explore Louisiana. They're safe! They'll be coming home! They traveled thousands and thousands of miles. They got to the headwaters of the Missouri River. They found the place where it splits up into three rivers.

Mama says Meriwether Lewis and William Clark got to the Pacific Ocean. An Indian girl, named Sacajawea, helped them to find horses so they could cross the mountains. And they're going to send some Indians to Washington City to meet Grand Papa.

And you know what happened after that? Grand Papa came from Washington City, home to Virginia, for his summer vacation. First he rode to Edgehill on his favorite horse, Castor. He came real early in the morning and he crept upstairs and he *caught me in bed!* I was fast asleep!

"Ellen Aroon!" said Grand Papa. "You're a sleepy-head. And I've caught you in bed again!"

Sister Anne told Grand Papa she *knew* he'd catch me in bed. She says I'm lazy, and I take too long dressing. But Mama and Grand Papa just laughed, and we all went downstairs for a breakfast of biscuits and jam.

Mama asked Grand Papa if he'd remembered to bring her the coffee cups. "I'll need them for the summer visitations," said Mama. She means all the visitors who come to see Grand Papa at Monticello in summer.

Sometimes Mama has to feed *fifty* people for dinner. But Grand Papa never turns strangers away, not if they have letters from friends of his. Sometimes the visitors stay for weeks and weeks. Grand Papa doesn't seem to mind.

Here's how Grand Papa spends his day resting at Monticello. He gets up at daybreak. If it's chilly his servant, Burwell, makes him a fire in the fireplace. Then Grand Papa reads, or writes letters before breakfast. Grand Papa has a machine in his study that makes a second copy of his letters while he writes them! It's called a polygraph.

Grand Papa has a leather chair that swivels around and

around. He invented it himself. He lets me turn around and around on it whenever I want.

"Grand Papa," I said, "it spins around just like a top or a whirligig." (A whirligig is a toy, and you blow in at one end of a hollow tube, and then a little paddle wheel at the other end spins around in a jet of air.)

"It *does* spin around like a whirligig, Ellen Aroon," said Grand Papa. "And that's just what the Feds have called it, Mr. Jefferson's *whirligig chair!*" And we have a good laugh at the Feds.

Sometimes Grand Papa reads in his study before breakfast. When Grand Papa is looking something up in his books, he sometimes takes down fifteen or twenty books at a time. Then he spreads them out on the floor and paces back and forth, from book to book. Here's how many books Grand Papa has in his library: 9,000. And here's all the different languages that Grand Papa can read: Latin, Greek, Anglo-Saxon, French, Spanish, Italian, and *English!*

Then Grand Papa goes to breakfast in the dining room. And then, around nine, he goes to the stables. I reckon Grand Papa loves horses more than any other animal in the world. He goes for long, long rides down by the river to see his mill, and he rides over his fields. Grand Papa looks over his crops for hours and hours, and doesn't come home until dinnertime, at three in the afternoon.

When there's company at dinner, sometimes we don't get up from the table until five o'clock. But before the sun goes down, we children go walking with Grand Papa.

Sometimes, at sunset, we sit on the portico, watching the sun go down over the Blue Ridge Mountains. When Grand Papa looks up at the ceiling, the inside weathervane, there, tells him which way the wind is blowing outdoors.

But tonight, when it gets dark enough, Grand Papa is going to take us up to the top of the house, into the dome, and let us look through his telescope. He's going to show us the rings of Saturn. Saturn is a planet, and it has these pretty bands, or rings, around it.

Right now, we're waiting for it to get good and dark. All of us children are playing a game with Grand Papa.

By now it's dark enough for all of us to go up into the dome, and look at the rings of Saturn. We all stand there quietly while Grand Papa focuses the lens of his telescope. Then at last he says, "There she is!" and lets me be the first to look. They look so pretty I just forget everything Mama ever told me, and I say: "They're mighty pretty, Mr. Mammoth!"

And Grand Papa looks at me, real deep into my eyes and we both begin to laugh. Grand Papa is still laughing when he takes me up to bed and kisses me good night. "Yes, mighty pretty," says Grand Papa. "Mighty pretty, Ellen Aroon!"

Rosa's Most Unforgettable Griggle

Jerry Holt

Rosa has a very special friend. Is her friend real or make-believe?

The first time Rosa ever heard of The Griggle, she was ten years old and had just moved to Las Cruces, New Mexico. Rosa went to public school, and that is where she first heard about The Griggle.

"The Griggle is twenty feet tall and purple," Harvey, a boy in her class, told her at recess one day. "It lives in a ditch outside of town and eats little kids."

A few days later, Rosa was eating her lunch with a girl named Beth. "The Griggle," Beth said, "is ten feet long and a hundred feet wide. It lives in a tree in the park."

"What else about it?" Rosa asked.

"It eats little kids," Beth said. She took a big bite out of her sandwich.

"How little?" Rosa asked.

"Ten and under," Beth told her.

During the next two weeks different pupils in the school told

Rosa about a hundred different places where The Griggle lived. She also got a lot of different ideas about how The Griggle was supposed to look. None of them agreed.

"I am pretty interested in The Griggle," Rosa told her mother one day after school.

"And what is The Griggle?" her mother asked.

"I don't know," said Rosa. "But it's very big and eats little kids who are ten and under."

"Well," said Rosa's mother, "You'll be eleven next January." Rosa's mother seemed to think The Griggle was a joke.

"I am *very* interested in The Griggle," Rosa told her father that evening. "But I can't find anything about it in the encyclopedia."

"Hmmmm," said her father. He was reading the newspaper.

Two days later, Rosa got a present from her aunt. When Rosa opened the box, she found a small camera. She took two pictures of her father and three of her mother. Then she took five pictures of her dog.

"I am going to save the last two pictures," Rosa thought to herself, "and take them of That Griggle."

On Saturday Rosa went to the park with her camera. The playground was full of other children, so she strolled into the wood. "I will climb a tall tree," she thought, "and see if I can spot That Griggle."

It was late in the afternoon when she perched upon a branch that she liked. The other children were starting to go home. "It's lonely up here," Rosa said out loud.

"It sure is," said another voice. Rosa looked around and almost fell out of the tree. The Griggle was sitting right beside her. It was about Rosa's size, furry all over, and bright blue in color.

"Allow me to introduce myself," said The Griggle.

"I know who you are" Rosa said. "You're The Griggle."

"True," The Griggle sighed.

"You're not any bigger than I am," Rosa said. "Why does everybody think you're so big?"

"I don't get out much," The Griggle replied.

"And why do you eat little kids?" Rosa demanded.

"Me? Eat little kids? Are you kidding?" said The Griggle.

"Well?" Rosa continued. "What *do* you eat?"

The Griggle reached over and grabbed Rosa's camera, then popped the camera into its mouth. "Cameras," The Griggle said.

"A fine thing," Rosa said. "Eating a poor little girl's camera."

"I can't help myself," The Griggle said. It pulled out a handkerchief and wiped its mouth.

"You ought to be ashamed," Rosa told it.

"I know," said The Griggle. "I know."

"A grown Griggle," Rosa chided.

"Enough!," The Griggle said, holding up its paw. "You'll make me cry."

Rosa looked around and saw that there wasn't as much sunlight in the trees as there had been. Then she became aware that the wood was filled with little chattering sounds. "What's going on out there?" she asked The Griggle. "What's making that noise?"

"Other Griggles," The Griggle said.

"You mean there are more than one of you?" Rosa said.

"There are Papa Griggles and Mama Griggles and Baby Griggles," The Griggle told her.

"You don't look like anybody's papa or mama to me," Rosa said.

"You're not exactly any Goldilocks yourself, Kid," The Griggle said.

"Perhaps I should be going home now," Rosa told The Griggle.

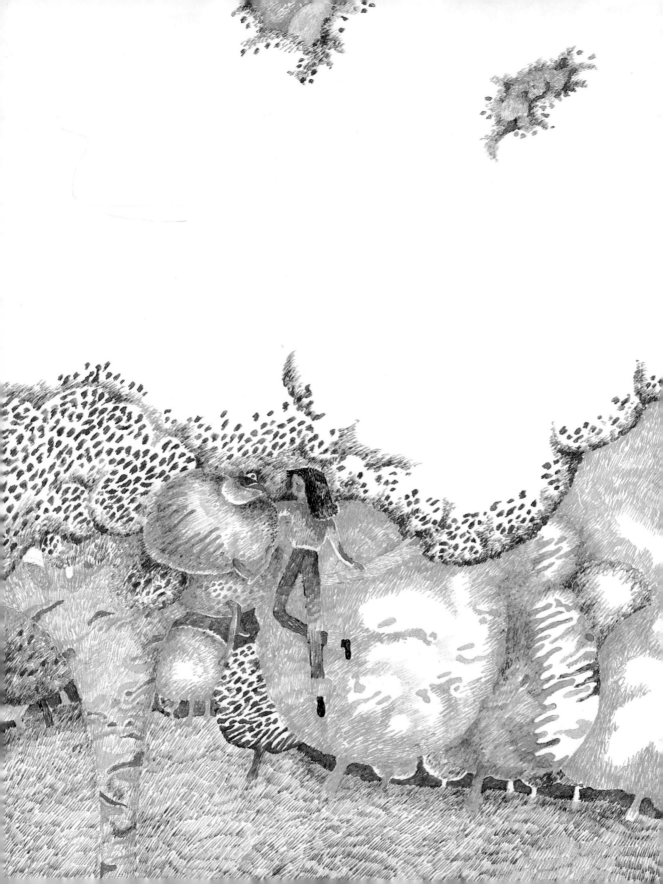

"It *is* getting late," The Griggle said. The Griggle very graciously helped Rosa down from the tree, saying, "I will walk with you to the edge of the wood."

And so The Griggle did. "Will you come back to visit?" The Griggle asked her. "Company usually just runs away."

"I will come back on Monday after school," Rosa said.

"Um — one thing," The Griggle said.

"What is it?" asked Rosa.

"I told a fib," The Griggle said. "There are no other Griggles but me. At least, none that I've met."

"And no more fibbing," Rosa said. "Friends don't fib to each other."

"It's a deal," The Griggle said, and disappeared into the wood.

Rosa didn't say anything at all, even to her parents, about meeting The Griggle. It was her secret. She listened to the other kids at school describe The Griggle the next Monday in all sorts of weird ways and just laughed to herself.

She thought instead about how lonely The Griggle must be and wondered if she ought to take some of her friends to meet it. She asked Harvey at lunch what he was doing after school.

"Going home," Harvey told her. "What did you have in mind?"

"I thought you might like to meet The Griggle," Rosa said.

Harvey said quickly, "I just remembered. I have to go to the dentist."

Harvey was afraid, and Rosa knew it. She asked her friend Beth the same question.

"Meet The Griggle?" Beth said. "Are you kidding? I'd be too scared."

So Rosa went to see The Griggle again by herself. She took

with her an apple left over from her lunch, a ukulele, her school reader, and half a bologna sandwich. The Griggle met her under the same tree in the wood. It ate the apple, showed no interest in the ukulele, and started to eat the book.

"Wait!" Rosa said. "Eat the bologna sandwich, not the book."

"Whatever you think," The Griggle said, beginning to munch away on the sandwich.

"Would you like me to read you a story from this book?" Rosa asked.

"Any stories about Griggles in there?" asked The Griggle, taking another bite of sandwich.

"It's possible. There are lots of different kinds of stories in this book," Rosa said.

"Are they true?" asked The Griggle.

"Some are true and some are not," Rosa said. "Both are important, though. If we like people in made-up stories and understand those people, maybe we'll like real people better and understand them better, too."

"Hmmmm," said The Griggle. It did not seem to understand much of what Rosa had said.

"I'll read you one," Rosa said, and she promptly read The Griggle a story about volcanoes.

"I understand volcanoes a lot better now. I never used to understand them, but now I think I do," said The Griggle.

"I have to go," Rosa told The Griggle. "We can read a lot of stories on Saturday."

Again The Griggle walked with Rosa to the edge of the wood. The Griggle gave her a very stately bow before it disappeared.

On the next Saturday Rosa read The Griggle five stories out of her book. One was about cowboys. The Griggle liked it the best and spent some time whooping about the wood, acting like a cowboy.

"I am getting interested in several things I never was interested in before," The Griggle said, a bit short of breath. It sank down under the tree beside Rosa.

"That's what reading stories can do for you," Rosa said. "I read about fifty a week myself."

"How many?" asked The Griggle.

"About five," Rosa said, lowering her eyes.

"Friends don't fib," The Griggle said. They both laughed, and Rosa asked The Griggle how it got its name.

"I have no idea," said The Griggle. "Maybe sometime you could write a story about that."

"Maybe sometime I will," Rosa said.

That was the only full Saturday that Rosa and The Griggle

spent together. She paid other visits, but kids in school get pretty busy in the wintertime. Rosa found that she was going whole days without thinking about The Griggle at all, and it made her upset with herself.

So on a Thursday afternoon after school, Rosa went to the wood. The wood seemed very dreary, now, and sad. She found The Griggle hunched over a magazine she had once brought it. The Griggle was trying to figure out some of the words by itself.

"This reading is no easy stuff," The Griggle told Rosa.

"You have to stick with it," Rosa agreed. She sat down in front of The Griggle and got out her handkerchief. "You have crumbs in your fur," she told it.

"I found half a pizza in the trash last night," The Griggle said. "I kind of go up to the park after dark, sometimes."

And then Rosa almost began to cry. So did The Griggle.

"You don't come to see me much anymore," The Griggle said, snuffling.

"I know," Rosa said.

"Pretty soon you won't come at all," The Griggle said.

"I know," Rosa told it.

They were quiet a moment. "Well, anyway," said The Griggle, "we had some good times. I never liked people before you read me those stories. I guess it was because they didn't like me."

"Do you like people now?" Rosa asked.

"Sure," said The Griggle, putting its head down in its fur. "Only I wish there were more like you, Rosa."

Rosa jumped up. "Come on," she said. "I'm taking you home, and you are going to meet my parents and all my friends."

I can't go past the edge of the wood in daylight," The Griggle said. "I'll disappear."

"No, you won't," Rosa said. She had The Griggle firmly by the paw. "Come on."

"Whatever happens," The Griggle said, "we still had some good times."

She held The Griggle's paw and ran through the wood. At its very edge, The Griggle disappeared.

Rosa got quite busy at school, but she went back to the wood at Thanksgiving and tried to find her friend. The Griggle was nowhere to be found. Rosa left a turkey sandwich for it. And at Christmas she left a little present: a book that was mostly pictures. She came back in a couple of days, and the present was gone. She never knew whether The Griggle got it or somebody else did.

That was a long time ago and Rosa is grown up now. If you asked her today, she couldn't tell you whether she really met That Griggle or read about it in a book like this one. She is sure of one thing, though: it doesn't make any difference whether The Griggle was real or not. And she wouldn't ever try to find The Griggle again. She knows that you can't find in space what you've lost in time. But you have lots of time. Perhaps you might find a Griggle in your local wood. Try it some Saturday, but don't take your camera. Just take your imagination and maybe half a bologna sandwich.

Touch the Sky

Otherwise Known as Sheila the Great

Judy Blume

Sheila likes to be called Sheila the Great. She wants to be the best at everything she does. But Sheila the Great has a weakness. She is afraid of water—terribly, embarrassingly afraid. The day finally arrives when she must meet her teacher, Marty, for her swimming test. Can she overcome her fear in front of her friends Mouse and the twins and still be able to call herself Sheila the Great?

This afternoon I am going to take my swimming test. I hope it rains. I hope it rains and pours until we leave here. But when I checked the sky, the sun was shining. And when I turned on the radio and listened to the weather report, there was no rain forecast.

So I hope I get sick and the doctor says I can't go in the water for ten days. But I feel fine. Except for my stomach, which keeps jumping all around.

So I hope that when I get to the pool this afternoon Marty won't be there. And no one will be able to find him. Then I will never have to take my swimming test!

But when we got to the pool, Marty was there, waiting for me. That's when I knew there was no getting out of it. I would have to take my Beginner's Test and if I drowned, I drowned! It was better not to think about it. Besides, chances were I wouldn't drown. Marty would probably save me. But if he had to jump in and save me in front of everyone, that would be as bad as drowning. Maybe even worse!

When I was in my suit, Mom said, "Good luck, Sheila. And please don't be nervous."

"Me . . . nervous?" I said. "Ha, ha. That's really funny."

When Marty saw me he called, "Hi, Sheila. All set?"

I didn't answer him.

"Okay, now here's all you have to do," Marty said. "First you'll jump in and swim across the deep end of the pool. Then you'll tread water for two minutes."

I don't know who Marty thought he was fooling. If he expected me to jump in and swim across the deep end of the pool, he was even nuttier than I thought. He was more than nutty. He was even more than crazy! He was also stupid, dumb, and an idiot!

"Are you listening to me?" Marty asked.

"Oh, sure," I told him. "I'm listening. But you know I can't swim across the whole pool!"

"Yes, you can," Marty said.

I folded my arms and gave him one of my best stares.

"You've got to try, Sheila. That's all I ask. You just can't give up without trying."

"Who's giving up?" I asked. "I can swim. You know that. You've seen me."

"Okay," Marty said. "So I know it. So now I want you to prove it to everyone by swimming across the pool."

"Maybe I just don't feel like it."

"Look, Sheila, there's absolutely nothing to be afraid of. If you can't make it, I'll be right there to help you."

"I am not afraid!"

"Then prove that you're not! Jump in right now and start swimming. I know you can make it. I have a lot of confidence in you."

I didn't answer him.

"Please, Sheila. Please try . . . for me."

I liked the way Marty said that. But when I looked across the pool, the other side seemed ten miles away. "You promise nothing bad will happen?" I asked.

"I promise," Marty said. "Word of honor. I'll even clear this section of the pool while you take your test."

"Do I have to keep my face in the water the whole time?"

"No, you can swim any way you want."

"How far is it across? About a mile?"

Marty laughed. "It's only forty feet."

"It looks like ten miles to me," I said.

"It's not. Tell you what . . . I'll count to three. Then you jump in and start swimming. I'll walk along the side of the pool and if you have any trouble, I'll pull you out."

"You'll really be near me?"

"Yes. I told you that. Now get ready."

I stood at the edge of the pool.

Marty counted. "One . . . and two . . . and three . . . jump!"

I didn't move.

"What are you waiting for?" Marty asked.

"I wasn't quite ready," I told him. "Let's try it again."

"Okay. Here we go. And one . . . and two . . . and three . . . jump!"

I held my nose and jumped in. When I came up, I looked for Marty. He was right where he said he'd be. "Swim . . . swim, . . ." he called.

I started. First I tried blowing bubbles, but I felt like I wasn't getting anywhere. So I kept my head out and swam like a dog. That way I could see what was going on. And I could keep an eye on Marty to make sure he followed me all the way across.

Every time I looked up at him, he yelled, "Go, Sheila, go!"

I swam past the low diving board. Then past the high one. And then I started to get tired. I couldn't get my arms all the way out of the water. And my legs didn't want to kick anymore. I looked up at Marty.

"Go, Sheila, go! Don't stop now!"

Marty was wrong. The pool wasn't forty feet across. It was really forty miles. I never should have tried it.

"Go . . . go. . . ."

Why didn't he just shut up? When I raised my head and looked straight across the pool, who did I see waiting for me but Mouse and the twins. They were yelling, "Go . . . go!" just like Marty. I wanted to tell them to stop. That I would never get to their side. This was very stupid. Soon I would be dead. Why didn't Marty pull me out? What was he waiting for? Couldn't he see I wasn't going to make it?

I tried to say, "I can't make it," but it came out so soft he didn't hear me.

He said, "That's it. Keep on going. . . ."

I can't . . . I can't . . . I thought. Then my hand touched the ladder.

Mouse and the twins were cheering and jumping up and down. Marty was yelling, "You made it! You made it! I knew you would!"

It was true. I swam across the deep end of the pool, and I was still alive! I really and truly did it! I tried to climb up the ladder, but Marty bent down and said, "Now all you've got to do is tread water for two minutes."

"No . . . no . . . let me up!"

"Relax, Sheila. You can do it. Just tread for two minutes."

Treading water is pretty easy. It's just like riding a bicycle, except you aren't on one. But I was so tired. I wanted to go to sleep.

Marty was holding a watch. He talked to me the whole time I was treading. He said, "That's it, Sheila. Only one more minute to go. And what's one little minute?"

When we got down to the last couple of seconds, Marty counted out loud. "Ten, nine, eight, seven, six, five, four, three, two, one. . . . Hurray! You did it! You did it!"

I climbed up the ladder, and Marty put his arms around me. Then he gave me a big kiss right in front of everybody, but I didn't mind. My mother ran over and wrapped me up in a towel, and Mouse and the twins dragged a lounge chair to me.

"I really did it?" I asked over and over.

"You sure did," Marty said.

"How about that?" Never mind that Mouse and the twins are already working on their Advanced cards. Never mind that Libby is practically a Junior Life Saver. Never mind that I will never dive like Betsy Ellis or stand on my hands under the water. *I can swim.* I proved it to everyone, including myself! I am Sunny Tubman, girl swimmer! I am Super Sheila the Swimming Wonder. I am . . . I am . . . I am. . . .

"Sheila, . . ." I heard my mother say. "Are you all right?"

I think I nodded.

Then another voice laughed and said, "She's asleep. That's all."

I think it was Marty. But I couldn't even open my eyes to thank him.

Patty Wilson's Magnificent Marathon

Sheila Cragg

When an athlete breaks a world's record in sports, it is a great accomplishment. Nearly everyone has personal goals to reach and records to break. For Patty Wilson, a teenage girl who has epilepsy, the goal is finishing a marathon race.

It used to be that when Patty Wilson ran, her arms and legs flopped like a rag doll's. She was very awkward. Why, she couldn't even throw a ball.

Perhaps this wasn't so bad. But Patty worried more about being clumsy than other people might. She came from a family of athletes. Her older brother, Richard, and her younger sister, Sandy, both enjoyed playing ball.

"I felt left out," Patty says. "I took dancing and thought that would help. They talked sports, and I didn't understand the world they were talking about."

Shyly at first, Patty began to run a mile with her father, Jim, who was always by her side, watching. Their runs were mild, a simple thing for someone who wasn't good in sports. But there was one more problem. Patty had a feared and misunderstood disease. She was epileptic. Her sickness and the way people fear those who have it became two reasons that pushed Patty to run her marathon.

Her first step to success came when she ran from her home in La Palma, California, to her grandparents' home in Los Angeles. Patty was thirteen, and she ran thirty miles.

In 1975 she and her dad ran a hundred miles, from La Palma to San Diego. When a newspaper wrote about the run, running became more of a challenge for Patty, and her determination became her reason for running.

As a freshman in high school, she joined the cross-country team. During her first meet, Patty had her first seizure while running. The weather was hot. A quarter-mile out, Patty began running like a machine. Her arms and legs marched up and down.

Jim and her mother, Dotty, were standing on the sidelines. They didn't know what to do. They couldn't — or wouldn't — go

among the runners and grab her. However, Patty finished the race. She was standing, but she was unconscious.

Jim and Dotty cooled her down with water and asked her questions: "What is your name? Do you know who I am? Where do you live?" There was no answer. Nearly an hour later, Patty came to, but she didn't remember anything about the race.

There would be more seizures, but Patty's doctor felt that she could keep on running — if someone else could always be with her.

Toward the end of the running season, she won her first race. She was invited to the Santa Barbara cross-country meet for high-school girls. "I was scared," Patty says. "It was a two-mile race over hilly terrain I'd never seen. The crowd was yelling 'Patty,' and I wondered why. I won it, and the team voted me Most Inspirational Runner."

Now was to come the second step for Patty, the next test. A few weeks later she and her dad ran 300 miles to Las Vegas. After the school year, they ran to San Francisco. They simply put one foot after the other for 508 hard miles.

In 1976-77, Patty, then a sophomore, ran on the men's cross-country team and the girls' track team, and Jim started talking about a run to Portland, Oregon. "I was against it," says Patty's mother. "I'd about lost Jim to heat stroke. I thought the San Francisco trip was hard enough."

Jim and Patty kept trying, though, and talked Dotty into helping them in their greatest challenge — a thousand-mile run from Buena Park, California, to Portland. To train for this trip, Patty and Jim ran 125 miles a week.

The Wilsons had kept Patty's epilepsy a secret. They feared she wouldn't be allowed to enter cross-country events and

marathons. Patty talked about it, but the newspapers and the public didn't.

Dotty explains why: "Patty's first seizure took place in her third-grade classroom. The teacher rushed out of the class and called the principal. They took Patty to the nurse's office. The children went home and told their parents about it, telling them the teacher said Patty had epilepsy. They came back with all sorts of stories. Children left Patty alone, and she didn't want to return to school.

"I figured that if that's the way a few act, then that's the way the public would act. We didn't even tell her grandparents for a long time."

Their doctor refused to use the word "epilepsy" when he spoke about Patty. He told the Wilsons that she had a seizure disorder, but they didn't know that he was speaking about epilepsy.

"I was scared of that word," Jim states. "I didn't know what it was. Now that I understand, it doesn't frighten me as much. Her epilepsy is so mild we don't think about her having it, nor does she. But she does have it, so why not help those who are less fortunate than we are?" The Wilsons did just that when they announced a month before her Portland run that Patty had epilepsy.

The date, June 18, was coming rapidly. Plans for the trip grew. The Wilsons needed help. Robert Bradach, a friend, took over. He raised money, found a van to rent, and talked with people in every city through which Jim and Patty planned to run. Much time was spent finding roads on which they could run and asking for police help.

On June 18, a crowd of people gathered to wish Patty well as she started her run to Oregon. Laughing and talking, she moved among the people. She turned toward the crowd, saluted, and then was off.

Several days later, at Port Hueneme, California, Jim and Dotty took Patty to the hospital. Her foot was X-rayed, and the doctor said that a cast should be put on the foot. A bone had been broken. The doctor warned that if she kept running she might never be able to run again.

"It was my decision to go on," says Patty. "Dad wanted me to go on. I could feel it. It was our dream."

Patty averaged thirty-one miles a day during the journey. She rose at 4:30 A.M. She and Jim were on the road and running by 6:00 A.M. They ran for five miles or more before taking short breaks.

"Patty pulled me along, and I pulled her along," Jim remembers. "We told each other stories, played games, and collected returnable bottles, and Patty practiced her Spanish."

After ten or fifteen miles, Patty and Jim would stop and have juices. They also took salt tablets. Breakfast and dinner were their only meals.

Patty's foot hurt her. It was swollen, and it barely fit into her shoe. Along with the drugs to control her epilepsy, Patty took pain medicine.

The wind, hills, and many other things made the trip hard. But all along the route, there were people to cheer Patty on.

At the end of the race, the Governor of Oregon ran the last mile with Patty. July 29 was set aside as Patty Wilson Day in Oregon. It was a special day for anyone who had ever worked to defeat a handicap. Patty had also set a world record. There was no official record of a woman running more than a hundred miles.

"I haven't been stopped because of my epilepsy. I never will!" Patty says. "This run was tough. It was a lot of races put together. Now, maybe people that are stopped because of epilepsy, or any other handicap, will try to do something they've always wanted to do."

Chuka's Hawk

Elizabeth B. Whitmore

Chuka always has to listen to Big Brother tell him how little he is. Chuka wants to find a way to prove to Big Brother that he is not so little. But what can Chuka do best to prove himself?

Chuka was playing on the roof of his mother's house, keeping well away from the corner where Big Brother's eagle was tied. The little Hopi boy looked at the sun. Only a small piece of it was showing above the mountains. Big Brother would come soon to feed the eagle.

Chuka stopped playing and stood watching the trail that led up to the mesa from the desert below. Soon he saw Big Brother coming, his bow and arrow in his hand, and his hunting bag full.

Big Brother climbed up the ladder onto the roof. His eagle pulled at the cord tied to its foot and screamed. Big Brother tossed meat to his eagle, and the eagle gulped it down.

Chuka hopped on one foot until his earrings bounced. "I want a pet eagle, too," he cried.

"Ho, you are too little." Big Brother laughed.

Mother was calling. They went down the ladder and into the house. Mother was dishing up stew from a pot in the fireplace. She handed a bowl to Big Brother, and he went to sit beside Father and

Grandfather. She handed one to Chuka. He sat near the fireplace. He dipped a piece of corn bread in the stew and ate it. Hm-m-m-m, it was good. Chuka was very, very hungry.

When they were finished, Chuka helped his mother clear away the bowls and wash them.

"Little boys do women's work," said Big Brother.

Chuka brought his blankets from the storeroom and spread them on the floor. Every night Grandfather told stories about the Hopi gods or the birds and animals. Tonight Grandfather told about adventures he had had when he was a boy. Chuka liked these stories best of all.

In the morning the thump, thump of Father's loom awakened Chuka. He rolled up his blankets and took them into the storeroom. He took a piece of cold corn bread and went out to play with Grandfather's new puppy, Bakito. When Big Brother came along, Chuka called, "Take me with you to herd the sheep in the desert, Big Brother."

"You are too little to walk so far," said Big Brother.

Chuka watched Big Brother start down the trail; then he went to see Uncle, who was working at his loom.

"You do not look happy, Chuka," said Uncle.

"I want a pet eagle," said Chuka. "Will you help me catch one?"

"An eagle cannot be tamed," said Uncle. "Your brother's eagle will never make a good pet. You can tame a hawk, if you are patient. Tonight I will make some prayer sticks. Tomorrow we will take the prayer sticks to the bird cemetery and hunt for a hawk."

The next morning Chuka and Uncle walked and walked. When they came to the bird cemetery, they placed the prayer sticks on the rock and made a prayer that Chuka would catch a hawk to tame.

Soon, Chuka heard bird sounds from high in the air. He looked up. "Those are hawks," Uncle said. "We are in a good place. Look for a hawk's nest in a tree."

Uncle walked ahead, looking and looking. Chuka saw a young hawk on the lowest branch of a tree. He watched it fly to the ground, snap up a grasshopper, and then fly back to the branch again.

Chuka caught four grasshoppers in a bush. He held them in his hand while he wriggled out of his shirt. Then he threw the grasshoppers on the ground in front of the hawk. The hawk swooped down to snap them up, and Chuka threw his shirt over the bird and caught him. The hawk struggled, but Chuka held on.

When Uncle came back, he asked, "What do you have there, Chuka?"

"A young hawk!" cried Chuka.

"You caught a hawk?" Uncle was surprised. "Our prayer and our prayer sticks were good."

They carried the hawk home and tied it by a cord on the housetop, as far away from Big Brother's eagle as they could. The hawk snapped its bill at the eagle.

"My hawk is not afraid of the eagle!" cried Chuka.

"Remember, you can tame him," said Uncle.

Every day Chuka went hunting. When he could shoot a mouse, he gave it to his hawk. When he couldn't, he caught grasshoppers. One day he stroked the hawk's head. It did not snap at him. After that, Chuka stroked the hawk's head whenever he fed him. The hawk liked Chuka. He rubbed his bill on Chuka's cheek and perched on Chuka's shoulder. After a while, Chuka untied the cord, climbed down the ladder, and took his hawk for a walk. The hawk perched on Chuka's shoulder. He was getting tame. The boy named his pet Wiki.

It was now time for Big Brother to learn how to weave blankets. Grandfather would teach him, and Father would herd the sheep.

"Come with me, Chuka," said Father. "It is time for you to learn to herd."

Every day Father and Chuka took the sheep out into the desert. Chuka learned to find grass and water for the sheep, and to keep the flock together. But he missed his hawk. He played with Wiki a little while every evening when he fed him.

After many weeks, Father said, "Bring the young dog Bakito today. He, too, must learn to work." As soon as Bakito had learned to herd, Father said, "Chuka, I am needed in the fields to plant the squash and corn and beans. You are big enough to herd the sheep. Bakito will help you watch over them."

Chuka felt very big and brave as he went down from the mesa with only Bakito. But when he was out in the desert, he did not feel big. He did not feel brave. The desert was hot and quiet and as empty as the sky. The day was as long as a week.

That night Chuka said to his father, "May I take Wiki with me when I go into the desert tomorrow?"

"Will you play with the hawk and forget to watch the sheep?" asked Father.

"Oh, no," said Chuka.

"Then you may take Wiki," said Father.

"Your hawk will fly away and leave you," said Big Brother.

The next morning when Chuka left the mesa, Wiki was perched on his shoulder. Every day Chuka herded the sheep, with Wiki and Bakito to help. Bakito chased rabbits and prairie dogs. Wiki found grasshoppers and snapped them up. Sometimes his sharp eyes saw a mouse, and he pounced on it. Once he heard other hawks high in the air. He left Chuka's shoulder and flew up, up until he was flying with them.

Chuka watched the hawks until he could not tell which one was Wiki. He was afraid Wiki would not come back. But soon a hawk began to fly down in big circles. When it was quite low, it swooped down and nipped Bakito on the ear. Bakito howled, but Chuka was so glad Wiki had come back that he laughed and laughed.

One day while Bakito was chasing rabbits and Wiki was playing with the other hawks high in the air, an animal chased the sheep. It looked like a dog, but Chuka knew it was a hungry coyote! It wanted a lamb to eat — one of his father's lambs!

Chuka found a big stick. He waved the stick at the coyote and shouted, but the coyote did not run away. It snarled and dashed at Chuka. He yelled and tried to hit the coyote with the stick, but it was too quick for him and dodged aside.

The sheep ran wild, baaing and bleating in panic.

"Bakito! Wiki! Help! Help!" screamed Chuka.

The hawk heard Chuka. Wiki did not sail down in big circles this time. He folded his wings and swooped down from the sky like an arrow. He dug his claws into the coyote's back, and nipped and nipped. The coyote howled. It ran away. Then Wiki flew to Chuka and perched on his shoulder. He rubbed Chuka's cheek with his bill.

Chuka laughed, and rubbed Wiki's head. Then Bakito rounded up the sheep. When he had them all together again, Chuka praised him and petted him.

That evening Chuka ate two bowls of beans cooked with onions and peppers for supper. He ate three big pieces of corn bread. When the dishes were cleared away, Chuka looked at Grandfather.

"Tonight *I* have a story to tell," he said.

Then Chuka told about the coyote. He told about the big stick. He told about Wiki and Bakito.

When the story was finished, Father said, "My son, you have done well. Tomorrow you may choose a lamb to have for your very own."

Big Brother went to the storeroom. He came back with his best arrow in his hand. He gave it to Chuka. "I will help you make a bigger bow," he said.

Chuka is busy. He and Wiki and Bakito drive the sheep out into the desert every morning. They watch them all day and drive them home in the evening. They are not afraid. They know they can take good care of the sheep.

Think About This:

1. How do you think Chuka felt when his father told him he was big enough to herd the sheep?
2. Why did Chuka's hawk come back to Chuka when the hawk had the chance to fly away and be free?
3. How do you suppose Chuka's brother felt about Chuka at the end of the story?

Cabezon

Robert Cruz

Two of Francisca's best traits are her courage and her ability to take over in an emergency. Little did she know she would have to use them on a holiday trip.

Mrs. Guterman, the fourth-grade teacher, stood by the classroom door as her pupils poured out into the hall. Francisca Garcia was the last to leave. *"Felices Pascuas,* Francisca," Mrs. Guterman said with a big smile. Francisca's dark eyes sparkled.

"Happy holiday to you, too, Mrs. Guterman," Francisca answered as she zipped her coat against the cold December wind.

"Are you leaving town?" Mrs. Guterman asked.

"Yes, Mamá and I are flying to Albuquerque to visit my grandparents, Papá and Mamá Garcia."

"It's a long way from Dallas to Albuquerque. But the airline pilots know the way. I'm sure you'll have a good trip."

Francisca laughed. "Mamá rented a plane for the holidays. She's the best pilot in the world."

"I'm sure she is. Have a nice trip. I'll see you in two weeks."

"Felices Pascuas." Francisca almost flew up the street. Her shiny black hair blew behind her as she ran. "Flying to Albuquerque . . . flying to Albuquerque," she sang in time to her feet on the sidewalk. She hardly slowed as she leaped up her front steps straight into the arms of her mother. *"Alto ahí,"* her mother said, laughing. "Stop! You're not flying yet." Her mother was a small, pretty woman only a few inches taller than Francisca.

"Oh, excuse me, Mamá. I was afraid I'd be late."

"You're not late. You're right on time. The suitcases and packages are in the car. Are you ready?"

"Ready? Am I!" Francisca shouted as she climbed into the car and fastened her seat belt.

It was a thirty-minute drive to the airport. Holiday lights brightened the houses and stores along the streets. "Flying to Albuquerque . . . flying to Albuquerque," went round and round in Francisca's head.

"Here we are," her mother said as she parked the car next to a bright red and green airplane.

Francisca and her mother quickly loaded the Christmas packages and the suitcases into the plane. "In you go," Francisca's mother said. Francisca climbed in. Her mother closed the door tight after her and climbed in on the other side. "Is your seat belt tight?" Francisca's mother asked as she pushed the starter button.

"Yes, Mamá."

The starter whined. The cold engine coughed for a moment and then started. The propeller became a blur as it turned faster and faster.

Soon they were cleared for take-off. Slowly at first, then more and more rapidly the little red and green plane rolled down the runway. The engine roared. The ground rushed by Francisca's window. The airplane gave a little bump, and Francisca knew they were in the air. Francisca and her mother were alone in the clear, blue winter sky. Far below, the trees were brown spots against the ground.

"What are you looking at, Francisca?"

"Oh, I'm just looking at the cars below on the highway. They look like tiny bugs," Francisca answered. Then she added with a grin, "But I guess our airplane looks tiny to the people in the cars."

"Yes," Francisca's mother said, "that is true. But you will have something more interesting to look at soon. I've been saving it as a surprise."

"A surprise? What is it, Mamá?"

"Do you remember where I was born? I've told you the story before — but not for a long time."

"In New Mexico?" Francisca answered.

"That's right. But where in New Mexico?"

Francisca thought for a moment as the plane flew through the air toward New Mexico.

"Oh, I remember now. You were born on a *rancho* near the mountain called Big Head. And you lived there until Papá and Mamá Garcia moved to Albuquerque."

"Good! But no one called it Big Head. Everyone used the Spanish name, *Cabezon*. And the mountain does look like a giant's head. It frightened me when I was a little girl. The place where I was born is gone now. And the town of Cabezon, at the foot of the mountain, is just a ghost town on the Rio Puerco."

"Mamá, *río* is river in Spanish. But I don't remember *puerco*. What does it mean?"

"It means *muddy*. Rio, *river* — Puerco, *muddy*. Rio Puerco, Muddy River."

Francisca's eyes shone with excitement. "That's my surprise! We are going to Cabezon, where you were born!"

Francisca's mother smiled. "I'm afraid ghost towns have no airports. But we are going to fly over the giant's head, Cabezon. And you will be able to see the town and the Rio Puerco."

On and on the little airplane flew. For a while Francisca stayed awake. But halfway across Texas, the smooth hum of the motor and the warm air inside the plane made her eyelids heavy. Soon she was asleep. Her mother leaned over, smoothed her hair, and smiled. "You are a good daughter, Francisca, even if you are asleep and cannot hear me tell you so."

Francisca's mother hummed happily to herself as she flew the little plane into New Mexico. Finally she gave Francisca's arm a gentle tug to awaken her. "Francisca, look below."

Francisca rubbed her eyes, yawned, and looked out the window. Beneath the plane a huge city was spread like a brightly colored quilt. The holiday lights below glittered. "What city is that?"

"That is Albuquerque, the home of your grandparents."

Francisca groaned, "Oh, no! We are here, and I missed Cabezon. Why didn't you wake me sooner?"

"You didn't miss Cabezon. It is on the other side of Albuquerque. We will fly over to Cabezon and then fly back to Albuquerque."

"Oh," Francisca said quietly. "I think I'll stay awake now."

"Look out the window, Francisca. Do you see that highway? It looks like a silver ribbon."

"Yes," Francisca answered.

"We will follow that highway for a short way and then we will

turn west. Then you see if you can find Cabezon, the giant's head."

In a moment Francisca felt the plane bank sharply to the left. She looked through the window at the ground below. There were few trees, only scrubby brush. The brown land was cut with *arroyos*. And from her seat in the airplane Francisca could see that they all finally ran into a dry riverbed. "Is that the Rio Puerco, Mamá?"

"Yes, and before long you should see Cabezon."

"It should be called dry river, not muddy river," Francisca said half to herself.

"I have seen a sudden storm fill the *arroyos* with rushing water and the river almost out of its banks," Francisca's mother said.

"Look!" Francisca shouted. "Look over there! Cabezon! And it looks just like. . . ."

Before she could finish, the airplane shook.

"Mamá, what? . . ."

Francisca's mother worked at the controls of the airplane. But the motor coughed once and died. For a moment the only sound was the whistling of the wind outside the plane. "Mayday! Mayday! This is November one eight niner seven Oscar. . . . She stopped. The radio was as dead as the engine. Francisca's mother spoke quietly as she fought to hold the plane level. "Francisca, tighten your seat belt as much as you can, and cover your face with your arms. We must land the plane."

Francisca's eyes grew wide with fear. "But there is no place to! . . ."

"Relax, my daughter," Francisca's mother said quietly. "We will be safely on the ground in a moment. Now do as I say."

For a second Francisca stared at the rough ground below. It was bare and unfriendly and frightening. The last thing Francisca

saw before she covered her face was Cabezon, the giant's head, standing in the distance like an ugly watchman.

Time seemed to stop for Francisca. She could hear only the wind. Then with a hard jolt they were on the ground. Brush whipped against the bottom of the plane as it bounced across the rough, rocky earth. Suddenly Francisca felt as if the ground had been jerked from beneath the plane. And almost at once there was a terrible, grinding crash as the plane nosed into the side of an *arroyo*. Francisca was thrown hard against her seat belt. She felt as if she would never breathe again.

The plane rested on its nose deep in the brushy *arroyo*. One wing hung down like the wing of an injured bird.

"Francisca . . . Francisca, can you hear me? Are you hurt?" Francisca's mother's voice shook a little.

Francisca fought for breath. Finally she was able to speak. "I . . . I think I'm OK," she said weakly.

Her mother sighed with relief and then groaned softly. Francisca turned quickly in her seat. "You're hurt, Mamá!" She could see the pain in her mother's eyes. "Where are you hurt?"

"My leg, Francisca. I think my leg is broken."

"But, Mamá, what can we do? We must be miles from town." Francisca could feel tears in her eyes. Her throat felt as if a large stone were stuck in it. She swallowed. "How can we call for help?"

"The radio is out. We will just have to wait for someone to find us."

Francisca felt a tear run down her cheek. *No,* she thought, *I must be brave. I am not hurt. I must be brave.* She felt another tear and turned toward the window.

She could not see beyond the edge of the deep, wide *arroyo* that the plane had crashed into. But around the plane, twisted bushes grew in bunches in the dry, brown soil.

"Francisca, . . ." her mother called softly.

Francisca quickly rubbed her eyes and turned to face her mother.

"Francisca, listen carefully. My leg is broken. I must depend on you." Her mother's voice was calm, but her face was pale. "I am sure we will not be missed before morning. So we must spend the night here."

"Can't we stay in the plane?" Francisca asked.

"No," her mother answered, "you should never stay in an *arroyo*. It is dry now, but if it should rain, the *arroyo* would fill with water rushing down to the Rio Puerco. We must get out of the plane. We will have to make a splint to hold my leg. That is why I must depend on you. Climb out of the plane and find two straight branches. While you are gone, I will get out of the airplane."

Francisca turned the handle on the door and pushed. She could not move it. It was stuck tight from the crash. She unfastened her seat belt and turned half around in her seat. Placing both feet against the door, she pushed hard. Still the door did not move. She gritted her teeth, pulled her legs back, and kicked as hard as she could. With a crack, the door popped open. Francisca dropped to the ground.

The sides of the *arroyo* were steep. Quickly she glanced around. There was nothing for a splint near the plane. "I must get out of this *arroyo*," she said to herself.

The rough ground made climbing hard. And three times she tripped and fell to her hands and knees to keep from falling backward. Using the scrubby brush to pull herself along, she neared the top of the *arroyo*. Here the sides were even steeper than before. Finally she grabbed a bush growing just at the edge.

And by throwing one leg over the top, she was able to pull herself out.

She lay on the cold, hard ground at the top. Her chest ached from the climb. Her breath came in painful gasps. Again she felt tears in her eyes.

In the *arroyo* she had been protected from the wind. But here in the open the north wind was bitter and cold. She got to her feet and stuck her hands in her coat pockets. Slowly she looked around.

In front of her rose the dark face of Cabezon, the giant's head. From the air it had been interesting. From the ground it was dark and frightening. She shivered and turned to look in the other direction. She gave a little squeak of surprise, for in the distance she saw a group of buildings dimly outlined against the evening sky. *People,* she thought. *There must be someone there.* Then she remembered — *Cabezon, the ghost town of Cabezon.*

She began to search for sticks for her mother's splint. But the sticks near the *arroyo* were small and brittle. Finally she turned toward the town of Cabezon.

Walking was hard. Rocks tripped Francisca at every step. And the rough ground made her trip again and again. Once she fell, and a dry bush scratched her face. With every breath needles seemed to poke into her chest. But she walked on.

At last she reached the empty town. The old wooden buildings seemed to lean with the cold north wind. Loose shutters squeaked and banged. Doors hung at odd angles. Quickly Francisca picked up two boards from a broken fence.

As she huddled out of the wind by one of the old buildings, she thought for a moment. *Here there is wood for a fire. Here we can get out of the wind. I must get Mamá here. But how? How?*

Then something caught her eye. A large wagon left behind by a child years before rested upside down in the dirt. Quickly she ran over to it. "Perhaps it will work," she muttered. "Perhaps . . . just perhaps." She turned the wagon over and tossed the boards in. Then she started back toward the plane and her mother.

The wagon squeaked and rattled as she pulled it over the rough ground. Her face and hands ached from the wind. In the west the sun was slowly setting. Dark clouds were moving toward Cabezon from the north.

At last she reached the edge of the *arroyo*. "Mamá!" she called. "Mamá!" But there was only the whistling of the cold wind. Francisca scrambled down into the *arroyo*. She ignored the brush that tore at her face and body. Her mother lay on the ground next to the plane. "Mamá!" she repeated as she knelt next to her mother.

"Francisca . . . Francisca, I must have fainted. Did you find some sticks?"

"Yes, Mamá. But are you all right?"

"I will be, I am sure. But we must get out of here."

Francisca fought her way up out of the *arroyo* again. Holding the boards, she climbed back down to her mother.

Her mother placed a board on each side of her hurt leg. Then she tore wide bands of cloth from the lining of her coat. "Francisca, you will have to help me. Wrap the cloth tightly around the boards. My leg must be held still between them. It cannot move."

Francisca began at her mother's ankle. Once her mother groaned softly. "Is that too tight, Mamá?" she asked.

"No . . . no, the leg is just sore. Go on. It must be tight."

At last Francisca finished. "But you still cannot walk on it," Francisca said. "How can you climb up the side of the *arroyo?*"

"I am afraid I must depend on you again, my daughter. You must take the place of my bad leg. Do you think you can?"

Before Francisca could answer, thunder rumbled from the direction of Cabezon. "I must, Mamá. I must," Francisca answered.

"Can you do one more thing, Francisca? We must have something to eat and something to drink. And we must have a fire to keep us warm. In the plane is the fruitcake we were taking to your grandparents and a Thermos of cocoa. And there should be some matches in the first-aid kit under the seat. Get all of those and carry them to the top of the *arroyo*."

Again Francisca slowly struggled to the top. Climbing was even harder with her load of food, cocoa, and the first-aid kit. And when she again reached the bottom, her legs were shaking. She dropped to the ground next to her mother. "Mamá, do you think someone will find us?"

"Of course," Francisca's mother answered. But she frowned when she looked at the dark clouds and listened to the wind. "Come, help me stand. We will climb to the top and find a place to spend the night."

Francisca forced herself to her feet.

"Just stand still," her mother said. "Let me get up and I will lean on you." Slowly, slowly she pulled herself to her feet. Her face grew pale from the pain in her leg. Twice she fell back against the airplane. At last she was up, standing on her good leg.

"How can I help?" Francisca asked.

"I will lean on your shoulder as we climb." She smiled at Francisca. "I will try to be as light as I can."

Carefully Francisca and her mother began to climb the steep side of the *arroyo*. Once Francisca's mother tripped over a rock, and they both fell forward. But little by little they climbed to the top. At the top, Francisca and her mother lay quietly on the ground.

"Francisca, we must move. It is growing dark. And we must find a place to stay warm. We will die in the open."

Francisca pulled herself to her feet. "We can stay in the ghost town. That is where I found the boards for your splint."

"I'm sorry, Francisca. I don't think I can walk that far. My leg is already beginning to swell."

"But, Mamá, you won't have to walk. I found a wagon. Look. Look behind you." Francisca's mother turned her head toward the wagon.

"We can try, Francisca. We can try. I don't think you can pull me all the way. But I can sit in the wagon and push with my good leg. Together we can do it."

Francisca helped her mother into the wagon. Then she placed the cake, Thermos, and first-aid kit in with her.

Slowly Francisca and her mother moved across the cold land. Before they were halfway to the old, deserted town, darkness fell. It was not the darkness of the city. It was like no darkness Francisca had ever seen. Even the stars were hidden by clouds. Far away a high-pitched howl broke the silence.

"Mamá, what was that?"

"Only a coyote, Francisca. When I was a little girl, they sang me to sleep each night." Her mother spoke calmly, but Francisca shivered.

Suddenly the moon broke through the clouds. It was almost as if someone had turned on a light. Francisca hardly saw it. She walked with her head down, using the last of her strength to pull the wagon.

"Francisca, look! I can see an old house! We are in the town."

Francisca lifted her head to look. But instead of stopping, she pulled the wagon through the open door. Once inside she stopped. "Mamá, I didn't think we could. . . . I was afraid to stop. I was afraid I couldn't start again."

"I know," her mother answered. "But together we did it." The weakness and pain in her mother's voice gave Francisca strength. She lifted her head and looked at their home for the night.

Moonlight flooded the small room. Francisca could make out an old fireplace at one end and a stack of wood next to it. In the first-aid kit she found some matches. In a moment she had built a fire in the old fireplace. "Mamá, how is your leg?"

"Help . . . help me out of the wagon," her mother answered weakly. Gently Francisca helped her mother to the floor. Then she lay down beside her. Three times during the night Francisca was awakened by the cold and tossed wood on the fire.

She awoke the next morning while it was still dark. The fire had died and she was chilled to the bone. Every muscle ached when she pulled herself to her feet. Quickly she rebuilt the fire. Then she sat next to the fireplace with her back against the wall.

"Francisca. . . ."

"Mamá, I didn't know you were awake."

"I was just thinking, Francisca. This is not what I had planned for our holiday treat. But even so, let's have some cake and cocoa for our breakfast." She pulled herself up and leaned against the wall next to her daughter. "Francisca, I was very proud of you last night. Had it not been for your strength, we might have frozen. But we are warm, and we have food and something to drink. I am sure we will be found today."

Together Francisca and her mother watched the gray of morning turn to bright sunlight. Francisca got up and walked to the door. "Mamá, I can see Cabezon, and . . . Mamá, I see an airplane over Cabezon!"

Francisca ran out into the deserted street and waved her arms. The airplane came closer and closer. For a moment Francisca thought it was turning away. But it made a big circle and flew back low over the ghost town. Twice the plane circled above Francisca. Then it was gone.

Francisca dashed into the house. "The plane left, Mamá! I know the pilot saw me, but the plane left!"

Francisca's mother smiled. "Of course, the plane left. But the pilot will send help. No one wants to land in this ghost town."

Francisca looked at her mother and laughed. "You're right, Mamá. No one wants to land in this ghost town."

Thank You, Jackie Robinson

Barbara Cohen

Jackie Robinson was one of the greatest baseball players on the Brooklyn Dodgers team. The boy who tells this story never expected to meet a famous sports star like Jackie Robinson. But one summer afternoon, a meeting between the great baseball star and the boy helps them achieve together a very special goal.

Today, Friday, I asked for my allowance and got my mother to give me the three dollars and fifty cents that was in the safe.

"I think that's too much to spend on a present for Davy," Mother said. "A dollar would be plenty."

"Mother!" I exclaimed. I was surprised. "If I had a thousand dollars, it wouldn't be too much to spend."

"It's your money, but I think you're crazy. You don't need to spend money to show love."

"It's the only way," I said. "They won't let me in to see him."

"It's your money," she repeated, shaking her head, but then she gave it to me.

The next day, Saturday, was of course the busiest day of the week at the inn. Even during July and August, the slow months, Saturday was sometimes busy. I was lucky. On this Saturday there was a wedding reception. What with Davy sick and the new cook not quite up to preparing a whole banquet, my mother had to be in six places at once. She really didn't have time to worry about us. It was one of those days when she just wanted us to go away somewhere and not bother her until it was time for Sara and me to help dish out the meal. I told her I was going over to Mickey's house and that I would stay there for dinner, but I'd come home before dark.

My mother nodded absently. "Have fun," she said and hurried off.

I suppose I could have told her where I was going. She might have been perfectly willing to let me go. She might have given me money for it. But I couldn't be sure.

I had gone into the kitchen real early in the morning, before anyone else was up, and made myself a couple of egg-salad sandwiches. I had them and my money and the new baseball in its little cardboard box. I walked the mile and a half to the bus station because there'd be no place to leave my bike if I rode there. I took the bus into New York City, and I took a subway to Ebbets Field.

You could see flags flying above the ball park when you climbed up out of the subway station. You had to walk three blocks and there you were. Inside it was as it always had been, as bright and green as ever, far away from the dirty streets that surrounded it, far away from all the world. In the excitement of being there, I almost forgot about Davy for a moment. I almost forgot why I had come. But then, when the Cubs' pitcher, Warren Hacker, began to warm up, I turned to Davy to ask him if he thought Shotton was going to give Jackie's sore heel a rest that day, but Davy wasn't there, and I remembered.

I thought maybe I'd better start trying right away. My chances might be better during batting practice than they would be later. I took my ball out of its box and hid the box under my seat. Then I walked around to the first-base side and climbed all the way down to the box seats right behind the dugout. I leaned over the rail. Billy Cox was trotting back to the dugout from home plate, where Erskine had been throwing to him.

I swallowed my heart, which seemed to be beating in my throat, and called out, "Billy, hey Billy," waving my ball as hard and as high as I could. But I was scared, and my voice wasn't very loud, and I don't think Billy Cox heard me. He went into the dugout.

This was getting me nowhere. I had to try something else before the game began and I'd really lost my chance. I looked around to see if there were any ushers nearby, and none was in sight. It was kind of early and the place hadn't really started to fill up yet.

I climbed up on the railing and then hauled myself onto the roof of the dugout.

I could have stood up and walked across the dugout roof to the edge, but I figured if I did that, an usher surely would see me. I crawled across the roof on my stomach until I came to the edge, and then I leaned over.

It was really very nice in the dugout. I had always kind of pictured it as being dug out of the dirt. But it had real walls and a floor and benches and a water cooler. Only trouble was, there were just a couple of guys in there—Eddie Miksis, and Billy Cox whom I'd seen out on the field a few minutes before. I was disappointed. I had certainly hoped for Campy's signature, and Gil Hodges', and Pee Wee Reese's, and of course Jackie Robinson's. But I figured Davy would be pleased with Miksis and Billy Cox, since their names on a ball would be more than he'd ever expected.

But no matter how hard I swallowed, my heart was still stuck in my throat. "Eddie," I called. "Eddie, Billy." Hardly any sound came out of my mouth at all.

And then all of a sudden I heard a voice calling real loud. Whoever it was didn't have any trouble getting the sound out of *his* mouth. "Hey you, kid, get down off that roof," the voice said. "What do you think you're doing?" I sat up and turned around. An angry usher was standing at the foot of the aisle, right by the railing, screaming at me. "Get yourself off that roof," he shouted. "Right now, or I'll throw you out of the ball park."

I crawled down as fast as I could. Boy, was I a mess. My pants and my striped shirt were covered with dust and dirt from that roof. I guess my face and arms weren't any too clean, either. I looked like a bum.

"I'm going to throw you out anyway," the usher said, "because you don't have a ticket."

I got real mad when I heard him say that. "You can't throw me out," I shouted back at him. "I've got as much right to be here as you have." I had suddenly found my voice. I was scared of the ball players, but this usher didn't frighten me one bit. I pulled my ticket stub out of my pocket. "See?" I said, pushing it into his face, "I certainly do have a ticket."

He made as if to take it out of my hand. I guess he wanted to look at it close, to make sure it was a stub from that day and not an old one I carried around in my pocket for emergencies. But I pulled my hand back.

"Oh, no, you don't," I said. "You can't take this ticket away from me. You won't give it back to me, and then you'll throw me out because I don't have a ticket!"

"You crazy, kid?" he asked, shaking his head. "This is what I get for working in Ebbets Field. A bunch of crazy people. Next year I'm applying for a job at the Polo Grounds."

"Go ahead," I said. "Who needs you?" I turned away from him and leaned over the rail.

"I better not see you on that roof again," the usher said. "I'll have my eye out for you—and so will all the other ushers."

"Don't worry," I said.

Then I felt his hand on my shoulder. "As a matter of fact, kid," he said, "I think I'll take you to your seat where you belong. Up in the stands where you can't make any trouble!"

Well, right then and there the whole deal would have gone up in smoke if old Jackie Robinson himself had not come trotting out onto the field from the dugout that very second. "Hey, Jackie," I called, "hey, Jackie," in a voice as loud as a crack of thunder.

He glanced over in the direction he could tell my voice was coming from, and I began to wave, still calling "Jackie, hey, Jackie."

He lifted up his hand, gave one wide wave, and smiled. "Hey, kid," he called, and continued on his way to the batting cage. In another instant he'd have been too busy with batting practice to pay any attention to me.

"Sign my ball," I screamed. "Sign my ball."

He seemed to stop briefly. I took this as a good sign. "You gotta," I went on. "Please, please, you gotta."

"He don't gotta do nothing," the usher said. "That's Jackie Robinson, and everyone knows that he don't gotta do nothing."

I went right on screaming.

"Come on, kid," the usher said, "we're getting out of here." He was a big usher who must have weighed about eight hundred pounds, and he began pulling me. But he couldn't shut me up.

"Please, Jackie, please," I went right on screaming.

It worked. Or something worked. If not my screaming, then maybe the sight of that monster usher trying to pull me up the aisle and little old me pulling against him for dear life.

"Let the kid go," Jackie Robinson said when he got to the railing. "All he wants is an autograph."

"He's a fresh kid," the usher said, but he let me go.

"Kids are supposed to be fresh," Jackie Robinson said.

I waved my ball in Jackie Robinson's face. "Gee, thanks, Mr. Robinson," I said. "Sign it, please."

"You got a pen?" he asked.

"A pen?" I could have kicked myself. "A pen?" I'd forgotten a pen! I turned to the usher. "You got a pen?"

"As it happens, I don't have one," the usher replied.

"Wait here," I said. "Wait right here, Mr. Robinson. I'll go find one."

Jackie Robinson laughed. "Sorry, kid, but I've got work to do. Another time, maybe."

"Please, Mr. Robinson," I said. "It's for my friend. My friend, Davy."

"Well, let Davy come and get his own autographs," he said. "Why should you do his dirty work for him?"

"He can't come," I said. The words came rushing out of me, one on top of the other. I had to tell Jackie Robinson all about it, before he went away. "Davy can't come because he's sick. He had a heart attack."

"A heart attack?" Jackie Robinson asked. "A kid had a heart attack?"

"He's not a kid," I explained. "He's sixty years old. He's my best friend. He's always loved the Dodgers, but lately he's loved them more than ever."

"How did this Davy get to be your best friend?" he asked.

So I told him. I told him everything, or as near to everything as I could tell in five minutes. I told him how Davy worked for my mother, and how I had no father, so it was Davy who took me to my first ball game. I told him how they wouldn't let me into the hospital to see Davy, and how we had always talked about catching a ball that was hit into the stands and getting it autographed.

Jackie listened silently, nodding every once in a while. When I was done at last, he said, "Well, now, kid, I'll tell you what. You keep this ball you brought with you. Keep it to play with. And borrow a pen from someone. Come back to the dugout the minute, the very second, the game is over, and I'll get you a real ball, one we played with, and I'll get all the guys to autograph it for you."

"Make sure it's one you hit," I said.

What nerve. I should have fainted dead away just because Jackie Robinson had spoken to me. However, he didn't seem to care.

"OK," he said, "*if* I hit one."

"You will," I said, "you will."

And he did. He broke the ball game wide open in the sixth inning when he hit a double to left field, scoring Rackley and Duke Snider. He scored himself when the Cubs pitcher, Warren Hacker, tried to pick him off second base. But Hacker overthrew, and Jackie, with that incredible speed he had, ran all the way home. The Dodgers scored six runs, and they scored them all in the sixth inning. They beat the Cubs, 6–1. They were hot, really hot, that day and that year.

But I didn't really watch the game as closely as I had all the others I'd been to see. I couldn't. My mind was on too many other things—on Jackie Robinson, on what was going to happen after the game was over, on that monster usher who I feared would yet find some way of spoiling things for me, but above all on Davy and the fact that he was missing all of the excitement.

And then I had to worry about getting hold of a pen. You could buy little pencils at the ball park for keeping box scores, but no pens.

It didn't look to me like the guys in the stands where I was sitting had pens with them anyway. I decided to walk over to the seats along the first-base line to see if any of those fans looked more like pen owners.

On my way I ran into this guy selling soda, and I decided to buy one in order to wash down the two egg-salad sandwiches I had eaten during the third inning.

This guy had a pen in his pocket. As a matter of fact, he had

two of them. "Look," I said to him as I paid him for my soda, "could I borrow one of those pens?"

"Sure," he said, handing it to me after he had put my money into his change machine. He stood there, waiting, like he expected me to hand it back to him after I was done with it.

"Look," I said again, "maybe I could sort of buy it from you."

"Buy it from me? You mean the pen?"

"Yeah."

"What do you want my pen for?"

"I need it because Jackie Robinson promised me that after the game he and all the other guys would autograph a ball for me."

"You don't say," the man remarked. I could tell he didn't believe me.

"It's true," I said. "Anyway, are you going to sell me your pen?"

"Sure. For a dollar."

I didn't have a dollar. I'd have to try something else. I started to walk away.

"Oh, don't be silly, kid," he called to me. "Here, take the pen.

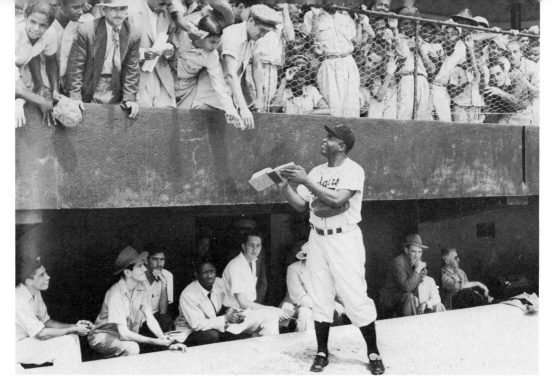

Keep it." It was a nice pen. It was shaped like a bat, and on it, it said, "Ebbets Field, Home of the Brooklyn Dodgers."

"Hey, mister, thanks," I said. "That's real nice of you." It seemed to me I ought to do something for him, so I added, "I think I'd like another soda." He sold me another. Between sipping first from one and then from the other and trying to watch the game, I made very slow progress down to the dugout. I got there just before the game ended in the top of the ninth.

I stood at the railing near the dugout, waiting, and sure enough, Jackie Robinson appeared around the corner of the building only a minute or two after Preacher Roe pitched that final out. All around me people were getting up to leave the ball park, but a lot of them stopped when they saw Jackie Robinson come to the rail to talk to me. Roy Campanella, Pee Wee Reese, and Gil Hodges were with him.

"Hi, kid," Jackie Robinson said. He was carrying a ball. It was covered with signatures. "Pee Wee here had a pen."

"And a good thing, too," Pee Wee said, "because most of the other guys left the field already."

"But these guys wanted to meet Davy's friend," Jackie Robinson said.

By that time, Preacher Roe had joined us at the railing. Jackie handed him the ball. "Hey, Preacher," he said, "got enough strength left in that arm to sign this ball for Davy's friend here?"

"Got a pen?" Preacher Roe asked.

I handed him the pen the man had given me. I was glad I hadn't gone through all the trouble of getting it for nothing.

"Not much room left on this ball," Roe said. He squirmed his name into a little empty space beneath Duke Snider's, and then he handed me both the pen and the ball. Everybody was waving programs and pens in the faces of the ball players who stood by the railing. But before they signed any of them, they all shook my hand. So did Jackie Robinson. I stood there, holding Davy's ball and watching while those guys signed the programs of the other fans. Finally, though, they'd had enough. They smiled and waved their hands and walked away. Jackie Robinson was the last one into the dugout and before he went around the corner, he turned and waved to me.

I waved back. "Thank you, Jackie Robinson," I called. "Thanks for everything." He nodded and smiled. I guess he heard me. I'm glad I remembered my manners before it was too late.

When everyone was gone, I looked down at the ball in my hands. Right between the rows of red seaming, Jackie Robinson had written, above his own signature, "For Davy. Get well soon." Then all the others had put their names around that.

I took the ball I had bought out of the box and put it in my pocket. I put the ball Jackie Robinson had given me in the box. Then I went home.

Giant Steps Through Time

Most people know that Thomas Edison invented the light bulb and that Benjamin Franklin discovered electricity. The light bulb and electricity were great steps forward. But there have been many others. Do you know who invented the zipper or the guitar? Read and decide for yourself whether these giant steps were taken quickly and easily or whether many people and much time were needed.

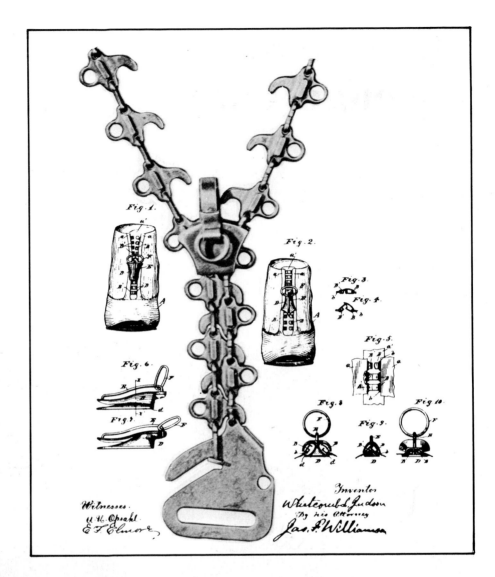

Zip 'Er Up

Hannah Campbell

Would you believe that the zipper started out as a way to fasten shoes? Well, it did. It was made by Whitcomb Judson. On August 29, 1893, he received a patent for a "Clasp Locker for Shoes."

When it was shown in the Chicago World's Fair in 1893, it was called a slide fastener.

Colonel Lewis Walker saw the invention and was interested in it. He agreed to build a factory where Judson could make it. The factory was called the Universal Fastener Company. Using the *Universal* meant lacing chains instead of laces into shoes. The chains could then be locked together with a slider. It was very hard to use, so no one wanted to buy it.

In 1905 Judson came up with another idea. This one was the *C-Curity*. It was stitched into clothing. It was much easier to use. The only trouble was that it would not stay closed.

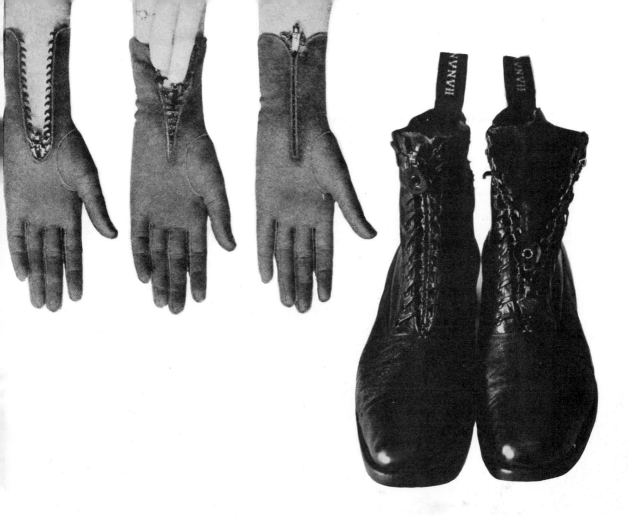

Gideon Sundback was given the job of making the *C-Curity* work. He improved it, so that it would stay shut. Even so, it sold mostly to theaters. This was because it helped actors change clothes more quickly. Sundback went back to the drawing board and began at the beginning. He finally came up with a fastener that worked. It was called the *Hookless No. 2*.

The public would not buy it, either. The really big break came when it was tested on a flying suit. When the test was over, all that was left of the suit was the *Hookless No. 2*. The Navy ordered 10,000 of them.

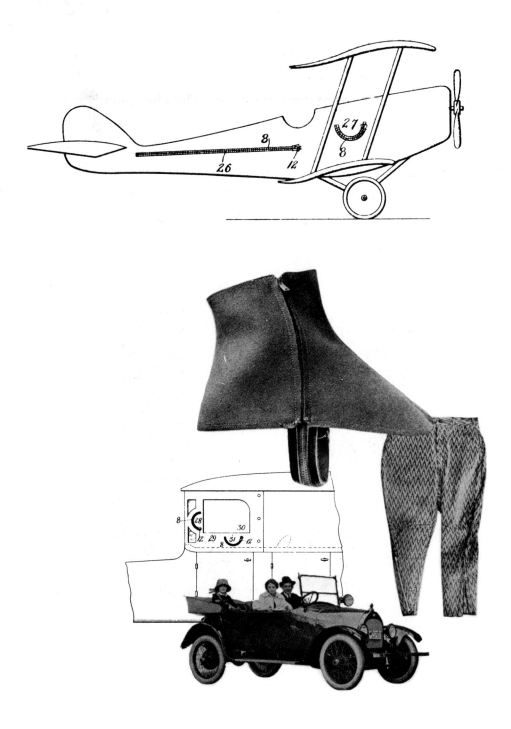

Suddenly, everyone wanted to use it. One company even used it to fasten rubber boots. The head of the company saw the boot. He opened and closed it several times. Then he shouted, "Zip 'er up!" That's how the zipper was named.

Today there are well over 150 uses for the zipper. In one plant alone, 700 miles of zipper tape are made every day.

To three men—Whitcomb Judson, Gideon Sundback, and Colonel Walker—we owe one of the most useful things of our time, the zipper.

The Music Box

Louisa Prince

One of the best-known instruments of music today is the guitar. It is used to make many kinds of music. It is used to play back-up or lead in a group. It is also played by itself. It has been around for hundreds of years.

No one knows exactly when the first one was made. But people who study history can guess. Something that looks a lot like it can be seen in old Egyptian paintings. The guitar, as we know it, more than likely appeared first in Spain. It later became known all over Europe and the Western world.

The guitar always has been, and still is, a box with a neck. Strings are stretched across the length of the box and up the length of the neck. They are fastened to pegs at the head.

The very early European guitars were made by hand from wood and had only four strings. Sometimes they were decorated with different kinds of wood. Others often had gold, silver, and mother-of-pearl. Because so much work went into making guitars, they cost a lot of money. Only the rich owned them.

Over hundreds of years, some changes were made in the guitar. Some of the changes have happened to make it sound better. Its size and shape have changed. Another change has come about in the number of strings. Most guitars today have six

strings instead of four. Some may have as many as twelve strings. Many of them are no longer made just by hand, so they don't cost as much as before. For this reason, many people own them today.

As long as music grows and changes, new instruments will appear. Who knows what might happen to the guitar.

Think About This:

1. How might the guitar have been invented?
2. Is the zipper an important invention? Why, or why not?
3. What are some other inventions that have been important to people all over the world?

Alvaro Pineda—Jockey

Evelyn M. Begley

Alvaro Pineda dreamed of becoming a jockey and of racing horses. But Alvaro did more than dream. He worked hard to reach his goal. Read about how Alvaro took that giant step by doing his best.

"You'll have to start at the bottom," the trainer said, looking at Alvaro. "We know you can ride well. But you've still got a lot to learn about horses—and that doesn't mean being a jockey right away."

Alvaro Pineda nodded eagerly.

"Yes, sir. That's all right, sir."

Looking around the tack room at the stirrups and bridles hanging on the walls, he could hardly believe this was happening. Ever since he had won his first race at the age of six, he had dreamed of becoming a jockey. Now at thirteen he was getting the chance to learn at last. How lucky he was that his uncle had written that letter to the Hipodromo manager in Mexico City! "Alvaro is a good rider, very small build, and has had a lot of experience in match races here in Guanajuato. He wants to be a jockey. Will you train him?" The manager had written back that Alvaro should come to Mexico City. Now here he was.

His father put his arm around Alvaro.

"We will be praying for you back home, son," he said. "Learn well."

As his father walked away, Alvaro remembered his mother and younger brothers and sisters. Guanajuato suddenly seemed farther away than two hundred miles. When would he return to the little house with the two quarter horses grazing out back?

"Come on, Alvaro," the trainer said. "I'll show you around and tell you what your job will be. You'll sleep in here, by the way. There's a bunk in that corner. By the time we're through with you there won't be *anything* you don't know about horses."

Life after that was horses, horses, and more horses. There were so many of them—different sizes, different colors, and (like people) different personalities. Alvaro was up around five every morning, sweeping out the stalls, putting in clean-smelling hay. He helped the grooms. He watched the workers as they exercised the horses in the morning before the races. He swept the stables and fed the guard dogs.

Every morning, the stables were busy. People came and went. The mornings rushed by for Alvaro. Then in the afternoons came the best time of all, the races themselves.

He loved the sound of the excited crowd. He liked to watch the jockeys in their colorful silks and caps. Deep inside he knew that he would be one of them when the right time came. He would win races too. Perhaps one day he would even race horses in the United States.

Alvaro was leading a horse out of its stall one morning when the trainer came up.

"How about exercising him today, Alvaro?" he asked.

"Yes, sir!"

He was ready for that. For days he had been sitting on the fence watching the horses exercise on the track.

"I can do it," he said to the trainer.

"Take it easy, then," the man said. "Let the horse go at its own pace. If it's tense, get off its neck and stand up in the stirrups."

Alvaro hoisted himself up into the saddle and sat proudly. How high up he was! Thoroughbred horses were much larger than the quarter horses his father had. He pressed his knees into the horse's sides and moved on to the track.

Every day after that he was on the track exercising. He learned how to groom the horses, too. After exercising them, he washed

them all over with warm soapy water and rinsed them with a hose. Then Alvaro hitched them up to a "walker" to dry. A walker is a large wheel with spars to hook the reins to. The horses walk in a circle, turning the wheel until their coats are dry.

Two years passed quickly. Alvaro was earning money and helping support the family at home in Guanajuato. Often he sent more than half his weekly pay packet home to his mother. Sometimes he went home for a visit.

On his first visit home, the whole family was lined up at the train station, waiting for him to arrive. All the children were jumping up and down with excitement. Everyone wanted to hug him as he stepped off the train. Alvaro felt happy.

Back at the track Alvaro often rode the horses fast during the exercise periods. The horses would run as though they were running a race. They would do what Alvaro wanted them to do. Alvaro's confidence increased daily. He knew he could handle any horse given him to ride. He started watching the jockeys more closely than ever. Surely the time would come soon when he too, dressed in silks, would sit proudly on a horse at the starting gate.

Alvaro Pineda was sixteen when that time came. It was his first race on a Thoroughbred.

"You'll be fine, Alvaro," the trainer said, patting his shoulder. "Remember all you've been taught. Go in there and *win*."

They were at the starting gate, waiting for the flag to drop and the gate to open. Alvaro's heart was pounding as he crouched over the neck of his horse. There were eleven other horses and riders lined up beside him. He wondered if they were as excited as he. He could feel the body of the horse under him. Suddenly a sense of confidence spread through him. This was a *good* animal, and he was a part of it.

The bell rang, the gate clanged open, and they were off. Alvaro was aware only of the power of his horse and the speed as they flew over the ground. There was a strange roaring in his ears. Alvaro realized it was the roar of the crowd. He bent lower over his horse's neck. They went faster and faster. They were ahead. He could feel that now. They were going to make it—going to be first! They flashed past the winning post. For the first time Alvaro knew the wonderful, heartbursting feeling of winning a big race.

After that day came many more races. In two years Alvaro was one of the best-known jockeys in Mexico City. By this time he was close friends with an American couple, racehorse owners. Alvaro had ridden many of their horses.

"How would you like to ride for us in the States?" his friends asked one day.

So Alvaro came to Southern California in 1964 at the age of eighteen. He rode all over the United States.

His hard work and determination helped Alvaro Pineda win the 1974 George Woolf Memorial Jockey Award at Santa Anita, California, for his successful racing career.

His friends and fans were shocked when Alvaro Pineda was killed in a freak accident at the track in 1975. He is remembered as a hard worker and a great rider.

Think About This:

1. Where did Alvaro race before coming to the United States?
2. What were some of Alvaro's duties at the racetrack before he became a jockey?
3. How did Alvaro reach his goal?
4. What goals have you worked hard to reach?

Alice in Wonderland

Lewis Carroll
(Adapted by Rochelle Hill)

Great achievements come in different shapes and sizes. One of the best achievements all people can share is the ability to use a lively imagination. Your imagination can carry you to faraway lands and strange places. In the play that follows, Alice is carried away to a strange place full of funny characters. As you read the play, think about what Alice does to meet her challenges.

Characters

ALICE
WHITE RABBIT
CATERPILLAR
DUCHESS
CHESHIRE CAT
MAD HATTER
MARCH HARE
DORMOUSE
QUEEN OF HEARTS
MOCK TURTLE
ALICE'S MOTHER, *offstage voice*

BEFORE RISE: *Soft music is heard, as* ALICE *enters left, in front of curtain, book in hand. She crosses right, sits on ground.*

ALICE: I think I'll just sit here awhile and read. (*Starts reading, begins to yawn.*) Dear me, I'm getting so sleepy. (*Continues reading, but shortly her head begins to nod, and she drops book, then stretches out on ground and falls asleep.* WHITE RABBIT *hops in right, as music stops.*)

RABBIT (*Looking at his large pocket watch*): I'm late, I'm late! (ALICE *wakes with a start, sits up.*) Oh, dear! I'm very late!

ALICE (*Rubbing her eyes in amazement*): A rabbit!

RABBIT (*Rushing past* ALICE): Out of my way, girl. I'm very late.

ALICE: Late for *what*, Mr. Rabbit?

RABBIT: No time to visit, my dear — she'll behead me for sure.

ALICE (*Alarmed*): Who'll behead you?

RABBIT (*Excitedly*): The Queen of Hearts, the jury, *everyone!* Oh, my ears and whiskers! What a terrible fate — a rabbit without his head! I'd surely look undignified.

ALICE: Mr. Rabbit, do tell me what is wrong! (*He ignores her and exits through the curtain. She calls after him.*) Mr. Rabbit, Mr. Rabbit! Come back! There he goes down that rabbit hole. (*She gets up, follows him through the curtain. After a moment, curtain opens.*)

*　　*　　*

SETTING: *A strange garden filled with flowers of extraordinary size and color. There is large rock up right, which hides an exit.*

AT RISE: ALICE *is sitting on ground.* CATERPILLAR *is lying on the rocks up right.* ALICE *does not see him at first.*

ALICE (*Bewildered*): Why, I must have fallen down the rabbit hole! I wonder how many miles it was. . . . It seemed I was falling right *through* the earth! And it was so dark. (*Looking around*) It seems I've hit the bottom, and it didn't hurt a bit! I'm not on the other side of the earth at all, but in someone's garden. (RABBIT *rushes in right.*)

RABBIT: I'm late.

ALICE: Why, Mr. Rabbit, what are *you* doing here?

RABBIT: *I* live here. And what, may I ask, are *you* doing in my garden?

ALICE: I seem to have fallen down your rabbit hole.

RABBIT: Yes, and through my house, and now you're trampling on my garden. Such a clumsy girl. You'd best fix yourself up and hurry along or you'll be late, too. (*He starts off left.*) Oh, dear, now I'm later than ever! (*He exits in a fluster.*)

ALICE (*Shouting after him*): Late for *what?* I just arrived! Mr. Rabbit, please come back! (*She gets up, starts after him, then stops.*) Mr. Rabbit! (*Angrily*) How rude of him! I asked him a civil question, and he deliberately ran off without giving me an answer!

CATERPILLAR (*Still calmly lying on rocks*): Who are *you?*

ALICE (*Startled, turning around*): I — I hardly know, sir, just at present. At least I know who I was when I got up this morning, but I think things must have changed many times since then. (*Walks over to him.*)

CATERPILLAR: What do you mean by that? Explain yourself.

ALICE: I can't explain *myself,* I'm afraid, sir, because I'm not myself.

CATERPILLAR: I don't understand.

ALICE: This morning, I was just a girl sitting by the river bank, and now I'm lost in this queer place.

CATERPILLAR: I don't find this place a bit queer.

ALICE: Well, your feelings may be different. All I know is, it seems very queer to *me!*

CATERPILLAR: You! Who are *you?*

ALICE (*Becoming irritated*): I think you ought to tell me who *you* are first.

CATERPILLAR: Why?

ALICE (*Frustrated*): Oh! (*She stamps her foot and starts off.*)

CATERPILLAR: Come back! I've something important to say!

ALICE (*Turning to him*): Yes?

CATERPILLAR (*Leaning forward, his nose practically touching hers*): Keep your temper.

ALICE: Is that all?

CATERPILLAR: No. You have no business standing in the Duchess's kitchen. (*ALICE looks around her, then becomes angry again.*)

ALICE: I'm *not* in the Duchess's kitchen! (*As ALICE argues with CATERPILLAR, DUCHESS and grinning CHESHIRE CAT enter left. They carry in table, large soup pot, spoon, and pepper. DUCHESS sits on ground beside table and begins stirring her soup, shaking pepper into it from time to time.*) I am standing in the White Rabbit's garden — wherever *that* is! There is no house here, and you can't have a kitchen without a house around it. And I don't know any duchess anyway!

CATERPILLAR: You certainly are standing in her kitchen. I must say you are very rude to barge into the Duchess's home without knocking.

ALICE: The Duchess! *Who* is *she?*

CATERPILLAR: *Who* are *you?* (*He disappears behind rocks and exits.*)

ALICE: Well, really! (*She begins sneezing.*) I certainly don't (*Sneezes*) understand him at all! (*She sneezes, then turns around to find herself standing before DUCHESS.*) Oh! My goodness! You must be the Duchess!

DUCHESS: Yes, and what do *you* have to say?

ALICE: Uh . . . uh . . . there's certainly too much pepper in that soup! Ach-oo!

DUCHESS: Nonsense. There's not nearly enough pepper in that soup. *(Shakes more into soup.)* Ach-oo! Not . . . ach-oo! . . . nearly enough.

ALICE *(Noticing* CHESHIRE CAT*)*: Please, would you tell me why your cat grins like that?

DUCHESS: It's a Cheshire cat, and that's why.

ALICE: I didn't know that Cheshire cats always grinned. In fact, I didn't know that cats *could* grin.

DUCHESS: They all can, and most of them do.

ALICE: What sort of people live about here?

CAT: In that direction *(Waving to right),* lives a Hatter; and in that direction *(Waving to left),* lives a March Hare. Visit either you like. They're both mad.

ALICE: But I don't want to visit *mad* people!

CAT: Oh, you can't help that. We're all mad here. I'm mad. You're mad.

ALICE: How do you know I'm mad?

CAT: You must be, or you wouldn't have come here.

ALICE: And how do you know that you're mad?

CAT: To begin with, a dog's not mad. You grant that?

ALICE: I suppose so.

CAT: Well, then, a dog growls when it's angry, and wags its tail when it's pleased. Now, *I* growl when I'm pleased, and wag my tail when I'm angry. Therefore, I'm mad.

ALICE: *I* call it purring, not growling.

CAT: Call it what you like. *(Pause)* Do you plan to play croquet with the Queen today?

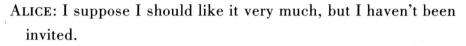

ALICE: I suppose I should like it very much, but I haven't been invited.

CAT: You'll see me there. *(There is a pause.* ALICE *turns to leave.)*

ALICE: Goodbye. (CAT *disappears slowly behind rock and exits. Singing and laughter are heard, then* MAD HATTER, MARCH HARE, *and* DORMOUSE *enter. They are carrying tea cups, teapot, etc., with which they set table.* ALICE *turns to watch them, then speaks to herself.)* Well, I certainly didn't have to go far at all. It's just as well. I'm not sure the cat's directions were very precise anyway. (MAD HATTER *and* MARCH HARE *sit on ground beside table at either side of sleeping* DORMOUSE *with their elbows resting on him. They see* ALICE *coming and begin shouting.)*

HATTER *and* HARE: No room! No room!

ALICE *(Indignantly)*: There's *plenty* of room! *(She sits on ground beside table.)*

HARE: It wasn't very civil of you to sit down without being invited.

ALICE: I didn't know it was *your* table — it's set for a great many more than three.

HATTER: Why is a raven like a writing desk?

ALICE: Oh, a riddle! I believe I can guess that.

HARE: Do you mean you think you can find the answer to it?

ALICE: Exactly so.

HARE: Then you should say what you mean.

ALICE: I do. At least — at least I mean what I say — that's the same thing, you know.

HATTER: Not the same thing a bit! Why you might just as well say that "I see what I eat" is the same thing as "I eat what I see."

HARE: You might just as well say that "I like what I get" is the same thing as "I get what I like."

DORMOUSE *(Talking in his sleep)*: You might just as well say that "I breathe when I sleep" is the same thing as "I sleep when I breathe."

HATTER *(To* DORMOUSE*)*: It *is* the same thing with you! *(*HATTER *and* HARE *drink their tea.* HATTER *takes his watch out of his pocket, shakes it several times, and holds it to his ear.)* What day of the month is it?

ALICE: The fourth.

HATTER: Two days wrong! *(To* HARE*)* I told you the butter wouldn't suit the works.

HARE: It was the *best* butter.

HATTER: Yes, but some crumbs must have fallen in as well. You shouldn't have put it in with the bread knife. *(*HARE *takes watch, shakes it, dips it into his tea, then puts it down.)*

HARE: It was the *best* butter, you know.

ALICE *(Looking at watch)*: What a funny watch! It tells the day of the month, and doesn't tell what o'clock it is!

HATTER: Why should it? Does *your* watch tell you what year it is?

ALICE: Of course not, but that's because it stays the same year for such a long time.

HATTER: Which is just the case with *mine*.

ALICE *(Puzzled)*: I don't quite understand you.

HATTER: The Dormouse is asleep again. *(He pretends to pour tea on* DORMOUSE's *nose.)*

DORMOUSE *(Talking in his sleep)*: Of course, of course, just what I was going to say myself.

HATTER *(To* ALICE*)*: Have you guessed the riddle yet?

ALICE: No, I give up. What's the answer?

HATTER: I haven't the slightest idea.

ALICE *(Exasperated)*: I think you might do something better with the time than wasting it in asking riddles that have no answers.

HATTER: If you knew Time as well as I do, you wouldn't talk about wasting *it*. It's *him!*

ALICE: I don't know what you mean.

HATTER: Of course not! I dare say you've never even spoken to Time!

ALICE: Perhaps not.

HATTER: If you only keep on good terms with him, he'll do almost anything you like with the clock. For instance, suppose it were nine o'clock in the morning, just in time to begin lessons; you'd

only have to whisper a hint to Time, and round goes the clock in a twinkling! Half past one, time for dinner!

HARE *(To himself)*: I only wish it were.

ALICE: That would be grand, certainly, but then — I shouldn't be hungry for it, you know.

HATTER: Not at first, perhaps, but you could keep it to a half past one as long as you liked.

ALICE: Is that the way *you* manage?

HATTER *(Sadly)*: Not I. We quarreled last March — just before *he* *(Pointing to* HARE*)* went mad, you know. It was at the great concert given by the Queen of Hearts, and I had to sing. *(Singing)*

Twinkle, Twinkle, little bat!

How I wonder where you're at!

You know the song, perhaps?

ALICE: I've heard something like it.

HATTER: It goes on, you know, in this way. *(Singing)*

Up above the world you fly,

Like a teatray in the sky,

Twinkle, twinkle —

DORMOUSE *(Singing in his sleep)*: Twinkle, twinkle, twinkle . . .

(He stops when HATTER *and* HARE *poke him.)*

HATTER: Well, I'd hardly finished the first verse when the Queen bawled out, "He's murdering the time! Off with his head!"

ALICE: How dreadfully savage!

HATTER: And ever since then, Time won't do a thing I ask! It's always six o'clock now.

ALICE: Is *that* the reason so many tea things are put out here?

HATTER *(Sighing)*: Yes, that's it. It's always teatime, and we've no time to wash the things between whiles.

ALICE: Then you keep moving round, I suppose.

HATTER: Exactly so, as the cups get used up.

ALICE: But when do you come to the beginning again?

HARE: There is no beginning.

ALICE: Of course there is! Everything must have a beginning!

HARE: Exactly so. The beginning already began, so the beginning
is used up and now there is no beginning.

ALICE: Then what do you do when you come to the end?

HATTER: There is no end until it finishes, and it's always six
o'clock, so we haven't gotten there yet.

ALICE: Then what do you do when you're in the *middle?*

HARE: Drink tea. Have some more.

ALICE: I've had nothing yet, so I can't take more.

HATTER: You mean you can't take less. It's very easy to take *more*
than nothing.

ALICE: Nobody asked *your* opinion.

HATTER: Now you're making personal remarks!

DORMOUSE: Twinkle, twinkle, twinkle —

ALICE: *(Stamping her foot)*: Oh! *(She walks away left in disgust,
then turns back, but they are busy trying to keep* DORMOUSE
from singing.) At any rate, I'll never go *there* again! It's the
stupidest tea party I was ever at in all my life! *(Goes and sulks
downstage left.)*

HARE: My cup is dirty. Everyone move to the next place.

HATTER: Move the other way! We've moved this way three times
already.

DORMOUSE: Twinkle, twinkle, twinkle, twinkle —

HARE: Put the Dormouse in the teapot and I'll sit at his place.

HATTER: But his things are slept on! It's much better to drink from
a dirty cup than one that's been slept on. *(*HATTER *stops talking,
when croquet players —* RABBIT, CATERPILLAR, DUCHESS,
CAT, *and* QUEEN OF HEARTS *—enter left, carrying mallets and*

hitting their balls ahead of them. They are yelling at each other.
RABBIT *hits croquet ball, which rolls to* HATTER, *who picks it up.)*

QUEEN OF HEARTS: Off with your head.

RABBIT: Who has my ball? Oh, my ears and whiskers, I shall never be able to play without my ball!

HATTER: I believe I have it. Care to join us for tea?

CATERPILLAR *(To* HATTER): Who are *you?*

QUEEN *(Seeing* HATTER *with ball)*: Off with his head! *(At this,* HATTER *and* HARE *run out right with their table and tea things.* DORMOUSE *is left behind, asleep. Croquet game continues without organization.)* Whose turn is it?

DUCHESS: Mine.

QUEEN: Off with your head! *(*HARE *and* HATTER *run back in, unnoticed by players, and carry* DORMOUSE *off.* QUEEN *notices* ALICE, *who has been dodging balls and people all this time.)* Who are you?

ALICE *(Startled, curtsying)*: My name is Alice, Your Majesty.

QUEEN *(Shouting as usual)*: Can you play croquet?

ALICE *(Shouting back)*: Yes!

QUEEN: Then play! Or off with your head!

ALICE: If you please, Your Majesty, I don't have a mallet or a ball. If you would be so kind as to — *(As she speaks, they all exit right, hitting their balls offstage as they go.* ALICE *is left alone on stage.)* Oh, well, at least I still have my head, and that's something to be grateful for! They're dreadfully fond of beheading people here. It's a great wonder that there's anyone left alive! *(*RABBIT *enters, scroll in hand.)*

RABBIT: The trial's beginning! Hear ye! The trial's beginning! *(Pointing to left)* The jury sits here. *(*RABBIT *is followed by* CATERPILLAR, DUCHESS, *carrying pepper shaker,* CAT, HAT-

TER, *carrying teacup,* HARE, *and* DORMOUSE. *Each carries slate and chalk.* TURTLE *joins jury.)*

ALICE *(To* RABBIT, *who is running around nervously)*: What trial is this? *(He ignores her. All attention is drawn to* QUEEN'*s entrance right. She takes her place at center.* ALICE *notices jury members writing on their slates.)* What are they doing? They can't have anything to write down before the trial begins.

RABBIT: They're putting down their names, for fear they will forget them before the end of the trial.

ALICE *(Quite loudly)*: Stupid things!

QUEEN: Silence in the court! Herald, read the accusation.

RABBIT *(Unrolling his scroll)*:

> The Queen of Hearts, she made some tarts,
>
> All on a summer day;
>
> The Knave of Hearts, he stole these tarts,
>
> And took them quite away!

QUEEN: Consider the verdict.

RABBIT: Not yet, not yet! There's a great deal to come before that.

QUEEN: Call the first witness.

RABBIT: Mad Hatter!

HATTER *(Stepping forward, teacup in hand)*: I beg your pardon, Your Majesty, for bringing my tea in, but I hadn't quite finished my tea when I was sent for.

QUEEN: You ought to have finished. When did you begin?

HATTER: Fourteenth of March, I *think* it was.

HARE: Fifteenth.

DORMOUSE: Sixteenth.

QUEEN *(To jury)*: Write that down. *(To HATTER)*: Take off that hat.

HATTER: It isn't mine.

QUEEN: Stolen!

HATTER *(Becoming nervous)*: I keep them to sell. I've none of my own. I'm a Hatter.

QUEEN: Give your evidence and don't be nervous, or I'll have you executed.

HATTER: I'm a poor man, Your Majesty, and I had just begun my tea, when the March Hare said —

HARE: I didn't!

HATTER: You did!

HARE: I deny it!

QUEEN: He denies it — leave that part out.

HATTER: Well, at any rate, the Dormouse said — um — and then I cut some more bread and butter —

CATERPILLAR: What did the Dormouse say?

HATTER: That I can't remember.

QUEEN: You *must* remember or I'll have you executed.

ALICE: That's not fair!

QUEEN: *Silence!* Or off with *your* head. (*ALICE steps back.* QUEEN *turns to* HATTER.) If that's all you know about it you may stand down.

HATTER: I'd rather finish my tea. (QUEEN *glares at him, and he sits down with jury.*)

QUEEN: Call the next witness!

RABBIT: Duchess! (*She steps forward with pepper shaker in her hand.*)

QUEEN: Give your evidence.

DUCHESS: Shan't.

QUEEN (*Shouting with anger*): What are tarts made of?

DUCHESS: Pepper, mostly.

DORMOUSE (*Sleepily*): Tea!

QUEEN: Collar that Dormouse! Behead him! Pinch him! Off with his whiskers! (*He promptly falls asleep.*) Never mind. Call the next witness.

RABBIT: Alice!

ALICE (*Stepping forward*): Yes?

QUEEN: What do you know of this business?

ALICE: Nothing.

QUEEN: Nothing *whatever?*

ALICE: Nothing whatever.

QUEEN (*To jury*): Consider your verdict.

ALICE: You can't consider the verdict yet. You haven't the proper evidence.

RABBIT: Of course we have. The jury has it all written down.

ALICE: If any one of them can explain the evidence, I'll give them a sixpence. *I* don't believe there's an atom of meaning in it!

QUEEN: If there's no meaning in it, that saves a world of trouble. We needn't try to find any.

CAT: Consider the verdict!

QUEEN: No, no! Sentence first — verdict afterward.

ALICE: Stuff and nonsense! The idea of having the sentence first!

QUEEN: *Off with her head!*

ALICE: Who cares for you? You're nothing but a pack of cards!

ALL *(Standing and pointing at* ALICE*)*: Guilty! *You* stole the tarts! Off with her head! Silly creatures indeed! *(Etc.) (Their voices grow louder and louder.* ALICE *backs away from them to edge of stage, sits and falls asleep, as curtain closes behind her. Voices stop abruptly. There is silence, then* ALICE'S MOTHER *is heard calling from off left.)*

MOTHER *(Off left)*: Alice! Alice, where are you?

ALICE *(Awakening)*: Oh, what a curious dream I've just had.

MOTHER *(Off left)*: Alice!

ALICE *(Calling off left)*: Coming, Mother! *(To herself, still quite sleepy and puzzled)* It all began when the White Rabbit ran across the bank — right over here — and he was so worried about being late. And I followed him —*(She looks around, as if trying to remember.)* I followed him over *here. (She goes center of curtain, but cannot find the opening.)* At least I *thought* there was a rabbit hole here — and somehow I fell down it ever so far and found myself among curious creatures in a strange land — a *wonder*-land! *(She runs off left, as soft music plays again.)*

Big Rig

Bill and Rosalie Brown

This selection is for you to read alone—for your own pleasure.
Clarence Carter is a truck driver who likes to do his job well.
Until Clarence finds a stowaway mouse aboard his rig, everything
is peaceful. The adventures of Clarence and Angelo the mouse
become more than just fun when they come face to face with a
blizzard and a stranded school bus.

Clarence Carter was mad. He pulled into the Chicago truck station. He had a load from Detroit. He was mad. But he was on time.

Clarence was always on time. He had never been late with a load. And he had never had a wreck on the highway. Not a single one. He was the best driver the company had.

Clarence drove slowly. He drove through the yard. He drove past other trucks. He drove past other trailers. He passed the sheds. Men were washing the big trucks with a steam hose. He drove by the shops. People were repairing engines. They were changing tires. The men all waved to him. Some shouted, "Hi, Clarence!"

Clarence didn't wave back. He didn't call "Hi!" He didn't speak to anyone. He wore his driver's cap. On it was his safe-driving pin. The hat was pulled down on his head. He looked straight in front of him.

The dispatcher came out of his office. He waved to a man driving a small machine. It was called a yard mule.

"Hey! Take Clarence's truck!" he said. "Put the trailer in Dock A. Get the load off."

Clarence climbed down from the cab. He was frowning.

"Well! What's wrong with you?" the man said.

"Look in my rig. Is that mouse in there again?" Clarence asked.

"Mouse? What mouse?"

"What mouse! The mouse that's trying to make me lose my job. That's what mouse!"

"Hm," the man said. "Never heard of a mouse in a truck before. What did he do?"

"It's all on my report," Clarence said. "Last trip, one package of salted peanuts nibbled. Mouse damage, ten cents. Trip before that, one box of soda crackers entered. And chewed. Damage, thirty cents. Before that, one sausage chewed up!"

The man laughed. "Oh! Is that all?"

"What do you mean is that all? When customers ship by truck, they count on the driver to get it through in good shape. They don't want it to be mouse-chewed."

The man scratched his head. He looked over at the people. They were emptying Clarence's trailer.

"Why don't you set a trap for him?" he asked.

"I've set box traps. And I've set other traps. A spring trap cut off one of his ears. Now he won't go near a trap!"

The man shook his head. "I guess he just likes you, Clarence. But maybe you could get away from him. You've been a long time on the Chicago-Detroit run. We could give you a different route."

"You mean . . . run away?"

"Why not? I could give you some other truck. One headed for Salt Lake. Or maybe clear to the West Coast."

"Yeh!" Clarence pointed his finger at the man. "I'll go west! That's what I'll do. You give me one headed west. I don't care if it hauls bulls. I don't care if it's a rag top. I'll go very far west! I'll never hear of that mouse again!"

A man came out of the trailer of Clarence's truck. He was holding two books. He had one in each hand.

"Hey, Carter!" the man yelled. "A mouse ate the backs off six copies of *Mother Goose!*"

The mouse was Angelo. His whiskers were bent. He had lost one ear in Clarence's trap. Angelo looked as if he'd been around. And he had. He had spent summers in Maine. Some winters he had spent in Florida. Once he climbed into a big truck in New Orleans. He rode all the way to New England in a large bundle of cotton. Then he went from New England to Chicago. He went in a load of new overalls.

At Chicago in the loading dock, Angelo had first seen Clarence. That was five days ago. Angelo had been looking out of a crack. It was in one of the loading docks. He had seen the kind look on Clarence's face. He had seen the button on Clarence's cap. It was a safe-driving button.

There's the driver for me, Angelo had thought. I'll follow him. Anywhere he goes.

Angelo loved the big trucks Clarence drove. He liked the hum of the fourteen giant tires on the road. He loved the smell that came from the engine. He thought it was sweeter than sausage or Limburger cheese.

Sometimes the truck would be loaded with stoves and refrigerators. It might carry shoes. It might carry roller skates. Or it might carry garbage cans. Angelo liked to poke around. He liked to see what there was. Once he came to a cardboard box. He chewed through the cardboard. And he found soda crackers.

This is a nice life for a mouse, Angelo thought.

The day Clarence decided to go west, Angelo was waiting. He was waiting just as he always was. He was in the middle of a pile of paper sacks on the floor. He watched Clarence talking to the workers. And he watched the workers talking to Clarence. He noticed everything carefully. He was trying to find the truck. Which one would Clarence drive this time?

The place was noisy. Little loading trucks buzzed in every direction. They carried stacks of boxes. Some men pushed hand trucks. All along the loading docks huge trucks were being filled.

Clarence and the dispatcher walked along the dock. They looked over the different trucks. They came to a refrigerator truck. The truck was large. In the front was a small box. There were holes high up on the box. This was the cooler for the warm refrigerator motor.

"Hey!" Clarence said. "Where's this going?"

"It's taking frozen foods. It's going to Salt Lake City," the man said.

Clarence walked around to the back. He looked inside. He saw frost on the walls. There was ice on the ceiling.

"A mouse would get mighty cold in there," he said. "Who's driving this?"

"Old Martin," the man said.

"Hm." Clarence rubbed his chin. "I think maybe I'll drive this. Is that all right with you?"

Angelo had ridden in big dry vans. He had ridden on flat racks. And he had ridden open tops. But he had never ridden in a cold truck. He slipped inside just before the workers closed the doors and sealed them.

"It's all buttoned up!" the dock checker called. Clarence drove off.

Angelo knew getting into that cold truck was a mistake before he was half a mile on the road to Salt Lake City. Frost was thick on the walls. And there was frost on the boxes of frozen food. It was dark inside. And it was cold. Angelo was losing the feeling in his one ear.

Angelo decided he'd better run around and warm up. But he couldn't move. He pulled. But his tail was frozen to the floor. He pulled. And he pulled. The skin of his tail almost came off. Finally he pulled loose.

Angelo looked all around. He was hunting for a way out. He looked everywhere. He looked along the walls. The truck was well sealed. It would stay freezing cold. There wasn't a crack around the doors. No warm air could get in.

Angelo started to climb up over the packages of frozen string beans and fish sticks. He went toward the top of the truck. Up in front he could hear the humming of the motor. It was louder than the hum of the tires on the highway. Then he saw a tiny crack of light. The light was near the roof.

The mouse pressed his nose to the crack. It was a hole. Small pipes went through. There was soft rubber around them. That kept the air out. Angelo squeezed past the rubber. He found himself in the box. He looked through the air holes. He could see the country go by.

This is just like Florida, Angelo thought. And he could go back to the food any time he was hungry.

Clarence would drive eight or ten hours. Then he would sleep in a motel. After that, he would drive another eight hours or so. At last he pulled into the loading yard. He was in Salt Lake City.

"Look back there. There may be a frozen mouse," he called to the yard worker. "Don't get him mixed up with the sausages."

Clarence went off to eat. When he came back his truck was empty. A man stuck his head out of the back.

"We didn't find a mouse. No mouse, frozen or alive," he said. He was holding up a package. "But we found these fish sticks. They're chewed open."

Clarence threw his driver's cap on the ground. Then he stamped on it.

"Where's the dispatcher?" he yelled. "I'll ask him to give me a tank truck. I'll take a tank truck. I'll go across the desert. I'd like to see a mouse that can live in one of those."

The man gave Clarence a tank truck. It was loaded. It was headed for San Francisco. Clarence could drive it clear through.

"It's a pajama wagon. There's a bed in the back. You can sleep right on the road. It's mostly desert now until you get to the mountains. This isn't the time of year for flash floods or desert storms. You shouldn't have any trouble. — Not until you reach the mountains."

"How about places to eat?" Clarence asked.

"Few and far between," the man said.

"Best one's Ma Bentley's. It's just before you reach the mountains. Won't get there until tomorrow night, though."

Clarence got a good sleep in a motel room. Then he bought two ham sandwiches. They were in a paper bag. He went back to his truck. It was loaded. It was ready to go.

Angelo was hidden under the loading dock. Angelo was watching. Clarence set his bag of sandwiches down. Then he climbed into the cab. He started the engine. He warmed it up. He climbed out again. He walked around the truck. He checked the air brakes. He checked the red stop lights. And he checked the other lights. He checked the air in the tires. He checked the horn. It blasted out loud and sudden. It made Angelo shake.

While Clarence was busy checking the tank truck, Angelo was busy. He was trying to get inside it. There were not any doors. There were not any openings.

Angelo looked up at the cab. It was very high up. The doors were closed. This time Angelo thought he was going to be left behind.

Then Angelo's nose began to wiggle. There was something good close by. He could smell fresh ham sandwiches. Angelo was hungry. He hadn't eaten anything since the fish sticks.

A corner of the paper bag was open. In one jump, Angelo was in. He was beside the sandwiches. He could chew through one of the wax paper wrappings. Suddenly, Clarence picked up the bag. He twisted the top closed tight. Then he tossed it into the cab.

Clarence climbed up into the truck. He put the lunch bag in the metal box of tools behind him. He slammed down the lid. He put the truck in low gear. It moved slowly out of the truck yard. This was the beginning of the long run to San Francisco.

The load was heavy. The truck rolled along. It picked up

speed. Clarence changed gears. Slowly he pulled out of town. He passed the last service stations. The highway went straight out. It went across the desert. A jack rabbit hopped across the road. Clarence slowed down a little. He didn't want to run over it.

Clarence would drive. Then he would sleep. He would stop. He would eat a quick meal. Then he would drive. And he would sleep again. Once he was nearly asleep in the bed. He was lying behind the seat. Suddenly he thought he heard a sound. It was in the box of tools. But then he thought, that mouse had really bothered him.

About noon the second day, Clarence saw the mountains. They were standing up blue ahead of him. He knew he had just about crossed the big desert. He could see the white snow on the peaks. Storm clouds were gathering around the mountains.

Clarence knew it was dangerous. A sleepy driver shouldn't drive over dangerous mountains. He would take a few hours' sleep. Then he would get a good dinner. He planned to push over the mountains in the night.

Clarence pulled over to a wide turnout. He remembered the ham sandwiches. He had bought them in Salt Lake City. They would be dry. But at least they would hold him until dinner time. He opened the box of tools. He pulled out the paper bag. He put his hand into it for a sandwich. His hand touched something soft. It was wiggling. He grabbed at it. He pulled it out of the bag. He held it high. He had a mouse by the tail. The mouse had only one ear.

"So that's what you look like!" Clarence said.

Angelo wiggled. He tried to get away.

"Oh, no! You don't!" Clarence said. "You've had your last ride in a big truck." He held the mouse up by his tail.

For once in his life, Angelo was scared. He hung there by his tail. He looked at Clarence's upside-down face. Even upside down, the face didn't look mean.

Clarence shook his finger right in front of Angelo's face.

"I really should feed you to a big cat. You've caused me a lot of trouble."

Clarence could feel Angelo shake. He shook right up through his tail.

"I know what I'll do," Clarence said. "I'll leave you out here. I'll leave you in the desert. The sun will bake you. The wind will freeze you. The animals will chase you. How do you like that?"

Angelo turned around. He looked out over the desert upside down. A bush was where the sky should be. He saw the far-off mountains. They pointed straight down.

Clarence got out. He started to put Angelo down on a rock.

Then he saw a black hawk. It was circling overhead. Clarence would be back in his truck. And that hawk would fly down on the mouse.

Clarence shook his head. "You're a no-good, one-eared pest," he said to Angelo. "But I can't stand blood." He started for the truck. He carried the mouse. He held him by the tail. "Come on. I'll find somewhere else to leave you. I'll leave you in some truck stop. Then you'll get lots to eat."

Clarence put Angelo back in the bag. Angelo was with the sandwiches. He wouldn't be hungry. Then he put the bag away. Clarence went to sleep.

It was almost dark when Clarence woke. He pulled the truck back to the highway. He headed toward the mountains again.

Cars and trucks had their lights on now. A truck met Clarence. It flashed its lights twice. Then it flashed them twice more. That was a new one to Clarence. He knew most of the truckers' signs. One sign was when a truck came up behind another truck and flashed its lights once. That meant it wanted to pass. Then the other truck flashed its lights. That showed it was safe to pass.

There were other signs, too. Three blinks of the lights was a sign. It meant there was danger ahead. There could be a wreck. Or there could be a washed-out bridge. But this sign—two flashes, and then two more. That was a new one. And Clarence knew that truckers didn't use light signs. Only for something important.

A half hour passed. Clarence met two more trucks. Both of them gave the same signal. Something was up there. Clarence knew that. But he didn't know what it was.

It was dark now. Clarence couldn't see the towering mountains. But they lay ahead. Far down the highway he could see bright lights. That was a truck-stop.

He could stop there. He could have dinner. He wanted to find

out what the flashes meant. And this would be the place to leave the mouse behind.

Two other trucks were pulled up in front of Ma Bentley's truckstop. They were lighted up like Christmas trees. They had red and gold lights.

Clarence brought his truck to a stop. The air brakes sighed. He locked the engine in low gear. Then he climbed out. He put blocks under the wheels. That way, the truck couldn't roll.

Then Clarence climbed back into the cab. He lifted the lid of the box of tools. He took out the paper bag. It held what was left of the ham sandwiches. He looked inside. The mouse was trying to hide. It was among the sandwich wrappings at the bottom.

"This is the end of the line for you," Clarence said. "You'll find a good home here. But you must behave yourself. Don't make trouble."

Clarence twisted the top of the bag tight again. He took it with him inside.

It was warm in Ma Bentley's. Clarence could smell soup and coffee. He could smell meat. It was frying with onions. He could smell fresh rolls.

Two other truck drivers were there. They were sitting on yellow stools at the counter. Clarence found a stool. He sat down. Ma Bentley put a glass of water, a knife, a fork, and a spoon in front of him. Clarence ordered fried chicken. He ordered coffee. He ordered two rolls. He set the bag with the mouse in it on the stool. It was beside him.

Clarence turned. He spoke to the other drivers.

"Can you tell me a secret? What kind of a sign is two and two flashes?"

The driver sitting next to Clarence looked up. He was surprised.

"You new here?"

Clarence nodded. "Just out from Chicago." The driver leaned toward another driver at the end of the counter. "Hey, Buckeye," he said. He jerked his head toward Clarence. "New man. Wants to know what kind of a sign two and two is."

Buckeye looked Clarence over carefully.

"You mean, flash, flash—flash, flash?—Like that?"

"That's right," Clarence said. "Flash, flash—flash, flash."

"That means snow on the mountain," Buckeye said. "It means to put iron on your tires. It means the guy who gave you the sign got through. But he's warning you."

Clarence frowned a little. "Well, I'm not the kind of driver who likes to take chances," he said. "And it would be nice sitting out the storm right here. . . ." He glanced down at the bag. The mouse was in it. He could hear Angelo move a little. "But I've got to get through tonight," he said firmly. "I've just got to."

Buckeye picked up a toothpick. "What kind of load have you got? What's so all-fired important?"

"A mouse," Clarence said. "I mean . . . !"

Buckeye sniffed.

The first driver turned around on his stool. He looked at Clarence.

"Did you ever hear of Highgear Higgins? He tried to get through the pass. He tried in the big snow of '56. He wrecked his truck. He wrecked it in the snow at the top. Old Highgear was there for three days. Finally the plows got him out. He had nothing to eat. He had only a load of canned tomatoes. He had to open the cans with a knife."

Clarence took a swallow of coffee. "I've got chains. And I'm used to snow," he said.

"The school bus was the last to go through," Ma Bentley said. "That was about four o'clock."

"Can a school bus do it? Then my truck can do it," Clarence said. He paid for his meal. He glanced down at the bag. The mouse was in it. Then he went out into the cold night. He put chains on his truck.

Back inside, Ma Bentley picked up her broom. She came out from behind the counter. She started to sweep the floor. She walked over to the window. She rubbed a clear place on the steamy glass with her apron. She could see Clarence. He was putting the chains on. Already a few snowflakes were drifting down. She shook her head.

"It's beginning to snow even down here," she said. She saw Clarence's bag. It was on the stool. "Oh, dear! That poor man left his lunch."

She picked up the bag. Then she hurried back behind the counter. "I'll drop half a dozen fresh rolls in here," she said. "I don't want to think of that nice fellow maybe stuck up there with nothing to eat."

She twisted the top of the bag. It was closed. "Here, Buck-eye," she said. She tossed him the bag. "Just drop this in the cab of that fellow's truck when you go out. He forgot it."

Clarence headed into the mountains. He could feel the wheels crushing the snow. He knew the sound of the chains. The drive wheels grabbed the ice on the highway. He could feel it, too, when the wheels slipped. Then the wheels grabbed again. The truck crept forward. The truck lights hardly picked up the white road. There was too much driving snow. There were no automobile tracks to follow.

What can I say, Clarence thought, if anything goes wrong? I can't say I drove over the mountains to get rid of a mouse.

Clarence knew one thing. He would be the last truck over that road. Others would wait until the storm ended. They would wait until the road was cleared. He thought about Highgear Higgins. Highgear spent three days in a pile of snow. And he had only canned tomatoes.

The drive wheels began to spin. The truck started to slip sideways.

"Easy now," Clarence said. He whirled the steering wheel. He turned the truck straight. It didn't slide off the road.

Clarence dimly made out a highway sign. The top of the mountain was only a quarter of a mile farther.

The howling wind was drifting snow across the road. It was still light enough to push through. The wheels packed it down. Some of the snow was piled beside the road. It looked deep enough to bury a big truck. The cab was warm. But just looking at the cold snow gave Clarence chills.

Angelo had eaten all the rolls he could. He was tired of being shut up. He was tired of the paper bag. He chewed a hole in the paper. Then he crawled out. For a while he sat quietly. He sat on the box of tools. The noise of the engine was loud.

Angelo saw Clarence's face in the dim light. It looked worried. Angelo didn't worry. Now he had ridden in the cab of a truck. He decided it was the best place to ride. He wanted to be near his good friend, Clarence. He thought he would find a good hiding place there to make a den.

Angelo found a nice place. It was behind the dash where there was a bundle of wires. He turned around a few times. This is just right, he thought. But there are too many wires.

Two wires were really in the way. Angelo began to chew on

them. The outside came off easily. But Angelo nearly broke his teeth. There was copper wire inside.

Suddenly there was a flash of light. The truck horn blasted loud. It almost knocked Angelo over on his one ear. He thought the sound would blast his hair off. He felt as if it were going to turn him inside out.

Clarence slapped at the horn button. The horn still blew. He shook the steering wheel. The sound didn't stop. He stamped on the floor.

Angelo jumped from under the dash. He jumped to the gear knob. Then he jumped up to Clarence's shoulder. Clarence grabbed for him. But Angelo jumped behind the seat.

Clarence didn't even have time to yell at Angelo. He had to give all his attention to the horn. He stopped the truck. He got his flashlight. He looked up under the dash. There he saw the two chewed wires. They were touching. He pulled the wires apart. The horn stopped.

"It would have served that mouse right if he'd had his head blown off," Clarence said. He leaned back in the driver's seat. He took a deep breath.

The truck horn was stopped. It was very quiet on the mountain. If anybody is up here to wake up, Clarence thought, that horn sure did wake them.

Then he heard another horn. It wasn't the horn of a big truck. It was an automobile horn. It sounded far away. It came in three short honks. It came over and over. Clarence knew that three short honks always mean "help."

Somebody is in trouble up here, he thought.

He opened the cab door. He climbed down into the snow. He listened. Everything was still. The wind was blowing the snow into deep piles. Clarence reached up into the cab. He touched the truck horn. It blasted out again. The automobile horn answered. There were three short honks. The sound was quiet. It sounded as if it were under a blanket.

That's not coming from far away, Clarence thought. It's coming out of the snow.

He walked along the road a little way. He flashed his light. Then he saw it. It was a bright spot of yellow. It was in a deep pile of snow.

"It's the school bus," Clarence said out loud. "It's full of kids!"

Clarence went back to the truck. He took out a shovel. The children yelled. They cheered. Clarence shoveled snow away from the bus.

Clarence finally got the door open. The driver climbed out.

"That truck horn was a sweet sound. It was the sweetest sound I ever heard," the driver said. "I heard it. And I knew we were safe. You can always count on a truck driver. They will get you out of trouble."

"Look," Clarence said. "We've got to get you out of here. The snow is getting deep. The plows might not get up here. Not for a few days."

It didn't take Clarence long. He separated his load from the cab. Then he backed his cab up. He backed up to the school bus. He hooked on a chain. Finally, he pulled the bus. It was back on the road.

"Now I'll break a path through the snow. I'll use my truck," Clarence told the driver. "You follow in my tracks. You'll be all right. We're at the top. It's all down from here on."

Clarence hooked up again. He pushed on past the school bus. The children were all laughing. They waved to him. The driver was shouting, "Thank you! Thank you!"

Clarence waved back. "Don't thank me! Thank my mouse!"

Later, Clarence had a chance to stop. He found Angelo hiding behind the seat. He picked up the mouse. He set Angelo on the dash by the front window.

"Now, mouse," Clarence said, "you and I are partners. You promise you won't chew up any more wiring, except when somebody needs help. You promise you won't get into any more loads.

And I'll feed you out of my lunch. I'm going to report this to the company. I'll tell them how you saved a school bus full of kids in a snow storm. You'll get a reward. You always have to chew on something. You can chew on that!"

Now Clarence and Angelo drive the highways. They carry coffee. They carry ice cream. They carry roller skates. They carry pickles. They carry electric heaters. They go from one city to another. Angelo has a place to sit. He sits by the front window. He can see the country. He has a box of crackers to eat. A small card hangs in the cab. It says:

To Clarence Carter's Mouse, for saving a school bus in a snow storm: full rights to ride in the cab of any Company truck.

The card is signed by the President. It is signed by the Manager. And it is signed by the Dispatcher. At the bottom it is signed by Clarence Carter, Driver.

Rikki-Tikki-Tavi _____

Rudyard Kipling

This selection is for you to read alone—for your own pleasure. If you enjoy this, you may want to read the entire collection of stories in The Jungle Book.

Rikki-tikki-tavi is a mongoose and like all mongooses, his eyes turn a frightening red when he is angry and face to face with his enemy, Nag, a very cunning and poisonous snake.

At the hole where he went in
Red Eye called to Wrinkle Skin.
Hear what little Red Eye saith:
"Nag, come up and dance with death!"

Eye to eye and head to head
    (Keep the measure, Nag).
This shall end when one is dead
    (At thy pleasure, Nag).
Turn for turn and twist for twist
    (Run and hide thee, Nag).
Hah! The hooded Death has missed!
    (Woe betide thee, Nag!)

This is the story of the great war that Rikki-tikki-tavi fought by himself in the big cottage in Segowlee cantonment. Darzee the Tailorbird helped him, and Chuchundra the Muskrat, who never comes out into the middle of the floor, but always creeps round by the wall, gave him helpful warnings. But Rikki-tikki did the real fighting.

He was a mongoose, rather like a little cat in his fur and his tail, but quite like a weasel in his head and his habits. His eyes and the end of his ever-moving nose were pink. He could scratch himself anywhere he pleased with any leg, front or back, that he chose to use. He could puff up his tail till it looked like a bottle brush, and his war cry as he wiggled through the long grass was: *Rikk-tikki-tikki-tikki-tchk!*

One day, a high summer flood washed him out of the ground-home where he lived with his father and mother, and carried him, kicking and clucking, down a roadside ditch. He found a little straw of grass floating there, and held to it tightly till he lost his senses. When he awakened, he was lying in the hot sun on the middle of a garden path, very bushed indeed. He heard a small boy saying, "Here's a dead mongoose. Let's have a funeral."

"No," said his mother, "let's take him in and dry him. Perhaps he isn't really dead."

They took him into the house, and a big man picked him up between his finger and thumb and said he was not dead but half choked. So they wrapped him in cotton wool, and warmed him over a little fire, and he opened his eyes and sneezed.

"Now," said the big man (he was an Englishman who had just moved into the cottage), "don't frighten him, and we'll see what he'll do."

It is the hardest thing in the world to frighten a mongoose, because he is eaten up from nose to tail with curiosity. The saying of all the mongoose family is "Run and find out," and Rikki-tikki was a true mongoose. He looked at the cotton wool, decided that it was not good to eat, ran all around the table, sat up and put his fur in order, scratched himself, and jumped on the small boy's shoulder.

"Don't be frightened, Teddy," said his father. "That's his way of making friends."

"Ouch! He's tickling under my chin," said Teddy.

Rikki-tikki looked down between the boy's collar and neck, snuffed at his ear, and climbed down to the floor, where he sat rubbing his nose.

"Good gracious," said Teddy's mother, "and that's a wild animal! I suppose he's so tame because we've been kind to him."

"All mongooses are like that," said her husband. "If Teddy doesn't pick him up by the tail, or try to put him in a cage, he'll run in and out of the house all day long. Let's give him something to eat."

They gave him a little piece of raw meat. Rikki-tikki liked it greatly, and when it was finished, he went out into the veranda and sat in the sunshine and puffed up his fur to make it dry to the roots. Then he felt better.

"There are more things to find out about in this house," he said to himself, "than all my family could find out in all their lives. I shall certainly stay and find out."

He spent all that day looking around the house. He nearly drowned himself in the bathtubs, put his nose into the ink on a writing table, and burned it on the end of the big man's cigar, for he climbed up in the big man's lap to see how writing was done. At night he ran into Teddy's room to watch how kerosene lamps were lighted, and when Teddy went to bed Rikki-tikki climbed up too. But he was always moving. He had to get up and attend to every noise all through the night, and find out what made it. Teddy's mother and father came in, the last thing, to look at their boy. Rikki-tikki was awake on the pillow. "I don't like that," said Teddy's mother. "He may bite the child."

"He'll do no such thing," said the father. "Teddy's safer with that little beast than if he had a big hound to watch him. If a snake came into the room now—"

But Teddy's mother wouldn't think of anything so awful.

Early in the morning Rikki-tikki came to early breakfast in the veranda riding on Teddy's shoulder. They gave him banana and some boiled egg. He sat on all their laps one after the other, because every well-brought-up mongoose always hopes to be a house mongoose some day and have rooms to run about in.

Then Rikki-tikki went out into the garden to see what was to be seen. It was a large garden, only half plowed, with bushes, as big as small huts, of Marshal Niel roses, lime and orange trees, clumps of bamboos, and thickets of high grass. Rikki-tikki licked his lips. "This is a wonderful hunting ground," he said, and his tail grew bottle-brushy at the thought of it. He hurried up and down the garden, snuffing here and there till he heard crying voices in a thornbush. It was Darzee the Tailorbird and his wife. They had made a beautiful nest by pulling two big leaves together and stitching them up the edges with fibers, and had filled the hollow with cotton and soft fluff. The nest moved from side to side, as they sat on the rim and sobbed.

"What is the matter?" asked Rikki-tikki.

"We are very miserable," said Darzee. "One of our babies fell out of the nest yesterday and Nag ate him."

"H'm!" said Rikki-tikki, "that is very sad—but I am a stranger here. Who is Nag?"

Darzee and his wife only cowered down in the nest without answering, for from the thick grass at the foot of the bush there came a low hiss—a frightening cold sound that made Rikki-tikki jump back two clear feet. Then inch by inch out of the grass rose up the head and spread hood of Nag, the big black cobra. He was five feet long from tongue to tail. When he had lifted one-third of himself clear of the ground, he moved from side to side exactly as a dandelion grass balances in the wind. He looked at Rikki-tikki with the wicked snake's eyes that never change their stare, no matter what the snake may be thinking of.

"Who is Nag?" said he. "*I* am Nag. The great God Brahm put his mark upon all our people, when the first cobra spread his hood to keep the sun off Brahm as he slept. Look, and be afraid!"

He spread out his hood more than ever. Rikki-tikki saw the

mark on the back of it that looks exactly like the eye part of a hook-and-eye fastening. He was afraid for the minute, but it is impossible for a mongoose to stay frightened for any length of time. Though Rikki-tikki had never met a live cobra before, his mother had fed him on dead ones, and he knew that all a grown mongoose's business in life was to fight and eat snakes. Nag knew that, too, and at the bottom of his cold heart he was afraid.

"Well," said Rikki-tikki, and his tail began to puff up again, "marks or no marks, do you think it is right for you to eat young birds out of a nest?"

Nag was thinking to himself, and watching the least little movement in the grass behind Rikki-tikki. He knew that mongooses in the garden were signs of death sooner or later for

him. He wanted to get Rikki-tikki off his guard. So he dropped his head a little, and put it on one side.

"Let us talk," he said. "You eat eggs. Why should not I eat birds?"

"Behind you! Look behind you!" sang Darzee.

Rikki-tikki knew better than to waste time in staring. He jumped up in the air as high as he could go, and just under him shot the head of Nagaina. She had crept up behind him as he was talking, to make an end of him. He heard her savage hiss as the stroke missed him. He came down almost across her back. If he had been an old mongoose he would have known that then was the time to break her back with one bite; but he was afraid of the terrible lashing return stroke of the snake. He bit, indeed, but he did not bite long enough, and he jumped clear of the whisking tail, leaving Nagaina torn and angry.

"Wicked, wicked Darzee!" said Nag, lashing up as high as he could reach toward the nest in the thorn bush. But Darzee had built it out of reach of snakes, and it only moved with the wind.

Rikki-tikki felt his eyes growing red and hot (when a mongoose's eyes grow red, he is angry). He sat back on his tail and hind legs like a little kangaroo, and looked all round him, and chattered with rage. But Nag and Nagaina were gone, into the grass. When a snake misses its stroke, it never says anything or gives any sign of what it means to do next. Rikki-tikki did not care to follow them. He did not feel sure that he could handle two snakes at once. So he ran off to the rocky path near the house, and sat down to think. It was a serious matter for him.

If you read the old books of natural history, you will find they say that when the mongoose fights the snake and the snake bites, the mongoose runs off and eats a plant that cures him. That is not true. The victory is only a matter of how quick is the eye and the foot—snake's blow against mongoose's jump—and as no eye can follow the moves of a snake's head when it strikes, this makes things much more wonderful than any magic plant. Rikki-tikki knew he was a young mongoose, and it made him all the more pleased to think that he had escaped a blow from behind.

He felt good about the fight, and when Teddy came running down the path, Rikki-tikki was ready to be petted. But just as Teddy was stooping, something wiggled a little in the dust, and a tiny voice said: "Be careful. I am Death!"

It was Karait, the dusty brown snake that lies for choice on the dusty earth; and his bite is poison like the cobra's. But he is so small that nobody thinks of him, and so he does the more harm to people.

Rikki-tikki's eyes grew red again, and he danced up to Karait with the strange rocking, swaying motion that was known to his family. It looks very funny, but it is an exactly balanced move that you can fly off from at any angle you please, and in dealing with snakes this is an advantage.

If Rikki-tikki had only known, he was doing a much more dangerous thing than fighting Nag. For Karait is so small, and can turn so quickly, that unless Rikki bit him close to the back of the head, he would get the return stroke in his eye or his lip. But Rikki did not know. His eyes were all red, and he rocked back and forth, looking for a good place to hold. Karait attacked. Rikki jumped sideways and tried to run in, but the wicked little dusty gray head lashed next to his shoulder. He had to jump over the body, and the head followed his heels close.

Teddy shouted to the house: "Oh, look here! Our mongoose is killing a snake." And Rikki-tikki heard a scream from Teddy's mother. His father ran out with a stick, but by the time he came up, Karait had lunged out once too far. Rikki-tikki had sprung, jumped on the snake's back, dropped his head far between his forelegs, bitten as high up the back as he could get hold, and rolled away.

That bite stopped Karait, and Rikki-tikki was just going to eat him up from the tail, after the way of his family at dinner, when he remembered that a full meal makes a slow mongoose. If he wanted all his strength and quickness ready, he must keep himself thin. He went away for a dust bath under the castor-oil bushes, while Teddy's father beat the dead Karait.

"What is the use of that?" thought Rikki-tikki. "I have settled it all."

And then Teddy's mother picked him up from the dust and hugged him, crying that he had saved Teddy from death. Teddy's

father said that he was a providence, and Teddy looked on with big scared eyes. Rikki-tikki thought all the bother rather funny because, of course, he did not understand. Teddy's mother might just as well have petted Teddy for playing in the dust. Rikki was truly enjoying himself.

That night at dinner, walking among the glasses on the table, he might have stuffed himself three times over with nice things. But he remembered Nag and Nagaina. Though it was very pleasant to be patted and petted by Teddy's mother, and to sit on Teddy's shoulder, his eyes would get red from time to time, and he would go off into his long war cry of *"Rikk-tikk-tikki-tikki-tchk!"*

Teddy carried him off to bed, and insisted on Rikki-tikki sleeping under his chin. Rikki-tikki was too well bred to bite or scratch. As soon as Teddy was asleep he went off for his nightly walk round the house, and in the dark he ran up against Chuchundra the Muskrat creeping around by the wall. Chuchundra is a brokenhearted little beast. He whimpers and cheeps all the night, trying to make up his mind to run into the middle of the room. But he never gets there.

"Don't kill me," said Chuchundra, almost weeping. "Rikki-tikki, don't kill me!"

"Do you think a snake-killer kills muskrats?" said Rikki-tikki scornfully.

"Those who kill snakes get killed by snakes," said Chuchundra more sorrowfully than ever. "And how am I to be sure that Nag won't mistake me for you some dark night?"

"There's not the least danger," said Rikki-tikki. "But Nag is in the garden, and I know you don't go there."

"My cousin Chua the Rat told me—" said Chuchundra, and then he stopped.

"Told you what?"

"H'sh! Nag is everywhere, Rikki-tikki. You should have talked to Chua in the garden."

"I didn't—so you must tell me. Quick, Chuchundra, or I'll bite you!"

Chuchundra sat down and cried till the tears rolled off his whiskers. "I am a very poor man," he sobbed. "I never had spirit enough to run out into the middle of the room. H'sh! I mustn't tell you anything. Can't you *hear*, Rikki-tikki?"

Rikki-tikki listened. The house was as still as still, but he thought he could just catch the faintest *scratch-scratch* in the world—a noise as faint as that of a wasp walking on a windowpane—the dry scratch of a snake's scales on brickwork.

"That's Nag or Nagaina," he said to himself, "and he is crawling into the bathroom sluice. You're right, Chuchundra; I should have talked to Chua."

He stole off to Teddy's bathroom, but there was nothing there, and then to Teddy's mother's bathroom. At the bottom of the smooth plaster wall there was a brick pulled out to make a sluice for the bath water, and as Rikki-tikki stole in by the masonry curb where the bath is put, he heard Nag and Nagaina whispering together outside in the moonlight.

"When the house is emptied of people," said Nagaina, "*he* will have to go away, and then the garden will be our own again. Go in quietly, and remember that the big man who killed Karait is the first one to bite. Then come out and tell me, and we will hunt for Rikki-tikki together."

"But are you sure that there is anything to be gained by killing the people?" said Nag.

"Everything. When there were no people in the cottage, did we have any mongoose in the garden? So long as the cottage is empty, we are king and queen of the garden; and remember that

as soon as my eggs in the melon bed hatch (as they may tomorrow), the children will need room and quiet."

"I had not thought of that," said Nag. "I will go, but there is no need that we should hunt for Rikki-tikki afterward. I will kill the big man and his wife, and the child if I can, and come away quietly. Then the cottage will be empty, and Rikki-tikki will go."

Rikki-tikki tingled all over with rage and hatred at this, and then Nag's head came through the sluice, and his five feet of cold body followed it. Angry as he was, Rikki-tikki was very frightened as he saw the size of the big cobra. Nag coiled himself up, raised his head, and looked into the bathroom in the dark, and Rikki could see his eyes glitter.

"Now, if I kill him here, Nagaina will know; and if I fight him on the open floor, the odds are in his favor. What am I to do?" said Rikki-tikki-tavi.

Nag waved back and forth, and then Rikki-tikki heard him drinking from the biggest water jar that was used to fill the bath. "That is good," said the snake. "Now, when Karait was killed, the big man had a stick. He may have that stick still, but when he comes in to bathe in the morning he will not have a stick. I shall wait here till he comes. Nagaina—do you hear me?—I shall wait here in the cool till daytime."

There was no answer from outside, so Rikki-tikki knew Nagaina had gone away. Nag coiled himself down, ring by ring, round the bulge at the bottom of the water jar, and Rikki-tikki stayed still as death. After an hour he began to move, muscle by muscle, toward the jar. Nag was asleep, and Rikki-tikki looked at his big back, wondering which would be the best place for a good hold. "If I don't break his back at the first jump," said Rikki, "he can still fight. And if he fights—O Rikki!" He looked at the thickness of the neck below the hood, but that was too much for him; and a bite near the tail would only make Nag savage.

"It must be the head," he said at last; "the head above the hood. And, when I am once there, I must not let go."

Then he jumped. The head was lying a little clear of the water jug, under the curve of it; and, as his teeth met, Rikki braced his back against the bulge of the red earthenware to hold down the head. This gave him just one second's purchase, and he made the most of it. Then he was banged back and forth as a rat is shaken by a dog—back and forth on the floor, up and down, and around in great circles. His eyes were red and he held on as the body cartwhipped over the floor, upsetting the tin dipper and the soap dish and the flesh brush, and banged against the tin side of the bath.

As he held he closed his jaws tighter and tighter. He was sure he would be banged to death, and, for the honor of his family, he wanted to be found with his teeth locked. He was dizzy, aching, and felt shaken to pieces when something went off like a clap of thunder just behind him. A hot wind knocked him senseless and red fire singed his fur. The big man had been wakened by the noise, and had fired both barrels of a shotgun into Nag just behind the hood.

Rikki-tikki held on with his eyes shut, for now he was quite sure he was dead. But the head did not move, and the big man picked him up and said, "It's the mongoose again, Alice. The little chap has saved *our* lives now."

Then Teddy's mother came in and saw what was left of Nag. Rikki-tikki dragged himself to Teddy's bedroom and spent half the rest of the night shaking himself tenderly to find out if he really was broken into forty pieces, as he fancied.

When morning came he was very stiff, but well pleased with his doings. "Now I have Nagaina to settle with, and she will be worse than five Nags. There's no knowing when the eggs she spoke of will hatch. Goodness! I must go and see Darzee," he said.

Without waiting for breakfast, Rikki-tikki ran to the thornbush where Darzee was singing a song of triumph at the top of his voice. The news of Nag's death was all over the garden, for the sweeper had thrown the body on the rubbish heap.

"Oh, you stupid bunch of feathers!" said Rikki-tikki angrily. "Is this the time to sing?"

"Nag is dead—is dead—is dead!" sang Darzee. "The great

Rikki-tikki caught him by the head and held fast. The big man brought the bang stick, and Nag fell in two pieces! He will never eat my babies again."

"All that's true enough. But where's Nagaina?" said Rikki-tikki, looking carefully round him.

"Nagaina came to the bathroom sluice and called for Nag," Darzee went on, "and Nag came out on the end of a stick—the sweeper picked him up on the end of a stick and threw him upon the rubbish pile. Let us sing about the great, the red-eyed Rikki-tikki!" And Darzee filled his throat and sang.

"If I could get up to your nest, I'd roll your babies out!" said

Rikki-tikki. "You don't know when to do the right thing at the right time. You're safe enough in your nest there, but it's war for me down here. Stop singing a minute, Darzee."

"For the great, the beautiful Rikki-tikki's sake I will stop," said Darzee. "What is it, O Killer of the Terrible Nag?"

"Where is Nagaina, for the second time?"

"On the rubbish pile by the stables, mourning for Nag. Great is Rikki-tikki with the white teeth."

"Bother my white teeth! Have you ever heard where she keeps her eggs?"

"In the melon bed, on the end nearest the wall, where the sun strikes nearly all day. She hid them there weeks ago."

"And you never thought it worth while to tell me? The end nearest the wall, you said?"

"Rikki-tikki, you are not going to eat her eggs?"

"Not eat exactly, no. Darzee, if you have a grain of sense you will fly off to the stables and pretend that your wing is broken, and let Nagaina chase you away to this bush. I must get to the melon bed. If I went there now she'd see me."

Darzee was a feather-brained little fellow who could never hold more than one idea at a time in his head. And just because he knew that Nagaina's children were born in eggs like his own, he didn't think at first that it was fair to kill them. But his wife was a sensible bird, and she knew that cobra's eggs meant young cobras later on. So she flew off from the nest, and left Darzee to keep the babies warm, and continue his song about the death of Nag.

She fluttered in front of Nagaina by the rubbish pile and cried out, "Oh, my wing is broken! The boy in the house threw a stone at me and broke it." Then she fluttered more desperately than ever.

Nagaina lifted up her head and hissed, "You warned Rikki-tikki when I would have killed him. Indeed and truly, you've

chosen a bad place to be lame in." And Nagaina moved toward Darzee's wife, slipping along over the dust.

"The boy broke it with a stone!" shrieked the pretending bird.

"Well! It may be some consolation to you when you're dead to know that I shall settle accounts with the boy. Nag lies on the rubbish pile this morning, but before night the boy in the house will lie very still. What is the use of running away? I am sure to catch you. Little fool, look at me!"

Darzee's wife knew better than to do *that*, for any bird who looks at a snake's eyes gets so frightened that she cannot move. So

she fluttered on, piping sorrowfully, and never leaving the ground, and Nagaina quickened her pace.

Rikki-tikki heard them going up the path from the stables, and he raced for the end of the melon patch near the wall. There, in the warm litter above the melons, very cunningly hidden, he found twenty-five eggs, about the size of a bantam's eggs, but with whitish skins instead of shells.

"I was not a day too soon," he said. He could see the baby snakes curled up inside the skin, and he knew that the minute they were hatched they could each kill a person or a mongoose. He bit off the tops of the eggs as fast as he could, taking care to crush the young cobras, and turned over the litter from time to time to see if he had missed any. At last there were only three eggs left, and Rikki-tikki began to laugh to himself, when he heard the bird screaming:

"Rikki-tikki, I led Nagaina toward the house, and she has gone into the veranda, and—oh, come quickly—she means killing!"

Rikki-tikki destroyed two eggs, and tumbled backward down the melon bed with the third egg in his mouth, and hurried to the veranda as fast as he could put foot to the ground. Teddy and his mother and father were there at early breakfast. Rikki-tikki saw that they were not eating anything. They sat stone-still, and their faces were white. Nagaina was coiled up on the matting by Teddy's chair, within easy striking reach of Teddy's bare leg, and she was swinging from side to side, singing a song of triumph.

"Son of the big man that killed Nag," she hissed, "stay still. I am not ready yet. Wait a little. Keep very still, all you three! If you move I strike, and if you do not move I strike. Oh, foolish people, who killed Nag!"

Teddy's eyes were fixed on his father, and all his father could do was whisper, "Sit still, Teddy. You mustn't move. Teddy, keep still."

Then Rikki-tikki came up and cried, "Turn round, Nagaina. Turn and fight!"

"All in good time," said she, without moving her eyes. "I will settle my account with *you* presently. Look at your friends, Rikki-tikki. They are still and white. They are afraid. They dare not move, and if you come a step nearer I strike."

"Look at your eggs," said Rikki-tikki, "in the melon bed near the wall. Go and look, Nagaina!"

The big snake turned half around, and saw the egg on the veranda. "Ah-h! Give it to me," she said.

Rikki-tikki put his paws one on each side of the egg, and his eyes were blood-red. "What price for a snake's egg? For a young cobra? For a young king cobra? For the last—the very last of the brood? The ants are eating all the others down by the melon bed."

Nagaina spun clear round, forgetting everything for the sake of the one egg. Rikki-tikki saw Teddy's father shoot out a big hand, catch Teddy by the shoulder, and drag him across the little table with the teacups, safe and out of reach of Nagaina.

"Tricked! Tricked! Tricked! *Rikk-tck-tck!*" chucked Rikki-tikki. "The boy is safe, and it was—I—I—I that caught Nag by the hood last night in the bathroom." Then he began to jump up and down, all four feet together, his head close to the floor. "He threw me back and forth, but he could not shake me off. He was dead before the big man blew him in two. I did it! *Rikki-tikki-tck-tck!* Come then, Nagaina. Come and fight with me. You shall not be lonely long."

Nagaina saw that she had lost her chance of killing Teddy, and the egg lay between Rikki-tikki's paws. "Give me the egg, Rikki-tikki. Give me the last of my eggs, and I will go away and never come back," she said, lowering her hood.

"Yes, you will go away, and you will never come back. For you will go to the rubbish pile with Nag. Fight! The big man has gone for his gun! Fight!"

Rikki-tikki was bounding all round Nagaina, keeping just out of reach of her stroke, his little eyes like hot coals. Nagaina gathered herself together and flung out at him. Rikki-tikki jumped up and backward. Again and again and again she struck. Each time her head came with a smack on the matting of the veranda

and she gathered herself together like a watch spring. Then Rikki-tikki danced in a circle to get behind her. Nagaina turned around to keep her head to his head, so that the rubbing of her tail on the matting sounded like dry leaves blown along by the wind.

He had forgotten the egg. It still lay on the veranda, and Nagaina came nearer and nearer to it, till at last, while Rikki-tikki was drawing breath, she caught it in her mouth, turned to the veranda steps, and shot like an arrow down the path, with Rikki-tikki behind her. When the cobra runs for her life, she goes like a whip flashing across a horse's neck. Rikki-tikki knew that he must catch her, or all the trouble would begin again.

She headed straight for the long grass by the thorn bush, and as he was running Rikki-tikki heard Darzee still singing his foolish little song of triumph. But Darzee's wife was wiser. She was off her nest as Nagaina came along, and flapped her wings about Nagaina's head. If Darzee had helped they might have turned her, but Nagaina only lowered her hood and went on. Still, that helpful instant brought Rikki-tikki up to her, and as he dived into the rat hole where she used to live, his little white teeth were clenched on her tail. He went down with her—and very few mongooses, however wise and old they may be, care to follow a cobra into its hole.

It was dark in the hole; and Rikki-tikki never knew when it might open out and give Nagaina room to turn and attack him. He held on savagely, and stuck out his feet to act as brakes on the dark bank of the hot, damp earth.

Then the grass by the mouth of the hole stopped waving, and Darzee said, "It is all over with Rikki-tikki! We must sing his death song. Great Rikki-tikki is dead! For Nagaina will surely kill him underground."

So he sang a very mournful song that he made up on the spur of the minute. Just as he got to the most touching part, the grass quivered again, and Rikki-tikki, covered with dirt, dragged himself out of the hole leg by leg, licking his whiskers. Darzee stopped with a little shout. Rikki-tikki shook some of the dust out of his fur and sneezed. "It is all over," he said. "Nagaina will never come out again." And the red ants that live between the grass stems heard him, and began to troop down one after another to see if he had spoken the truth.

Rikki-tikki curled himself up in the grass and slept where he was—slept and slept till it was late in the afternoon, for he had done a hard day's work.

"Now," he said, when he awoke, "I will go back to the house. Tell the Coppersmith, Darzee, and he will tell the garden that Nagaina is dead."

The Coppersmith is a bird who makes a noise exactly like the beating of a little hammer on a copper pot. The reason he is always making it is because he is the town crier to every Indian garden. He tells all the news to everybody who cares to listen. As Rikki-tikki went up the path, he heard the Coppersmith's "attention" notes like a tiny dinner gong, and then the steady *"Ding-dong-tock!* Nag is dead—*dong!* Nagaina is dead! *Ding-dong-tock!"* That set all the birds in the garden singing, and the frogs croaking, for Nag and Nagaina used to eat frogs as well as little birds.

When Rikki got to the house, Teddy and Teddy's mother and Teddy's father came out and almost cried over him; and that night he ate all that was given him till he could eat no more, and went to bed on Teddy's shoulder, where Teddy's mother saw him when she came to look late at night.

"He saved our lives and Teddy's life," she said to her husband. "Just think, he saved all our lives."

Rikki-tikki woke up with a jump, for the mongooses are light sleepers.

"Oh, it's you," said he. "What are you bothering for? All the cobras are dead. And if they weren't, I'm here."

Rikki-tikki had a right to be proud of himself. But he did not grow too proud, and he kept that garden as a mongoose should keep it, with tooth and jump and spring and bite, till never a cobra dared show its head inside the walls.

Glossary

Selections from *The H B J School Dictionary*, copyright © 1977, 1972, 1968 by Harcourt Brace Jovanovich, Inc., are reprinted by permission of the publisher.

Key to Pronunciation

Listed below are diacritical symbols and key words. The boldface letters in the key words represent the sounds indicated by the symbols.

/ā/	**cake**	/d/	**d**uck
/a/	**hat**	/ē/	**b**ean
/ä/	**father**	/e/	**pet**
/är/	**car**	/f/	**fun**
/âr/	**care**	/g/	**go**
/b/	**boy**	/gz/	e**x**act
/ch/	**church**	/h/	**home**
/(h)w/	**wh**ite	/ou/	**out**
/ī/	**pie**	/p/	**pet**
/i/	**pig**	/r/	**run**
/ir/	**dear**	/s/	**see**
/j/	**jump**	/sh/	**ship**
/k/	**kite**	/t/	**top**
/ks/	bo**x**	/th/	**thin**
/kw/	**qu**it	/th/	**th**is
/l/	**look**	/u/	**nut**
/m/	**man**	/ûr/	**fur**
/n/	**not**	/v/	**vine**
/ng/	si**ng**	/w/	**will**
/ō/	**rope**	/y/	**yes**
/o/	**top**	/yoo/	**use**
/ô/	**saw**	/z/	**zoo**
/oi/	**oil**	/zh/	a**z**ure
/oo/	**moon**	/ə/	**above**
/oo/	**book**		**circus**
/ôr/	**fork**	/ər/	**bitter**

Aa

a·brupt [ə·brupt'] *adj.* 1. Sudden; hasty: We could not understand their angry, *abrupt* departure. 2. Rude or curt, as in speech. —**a·brupt'ly** *adv.*

ac·com·plish·ment [ə·kom'plish·mənt] *n.* 1. Something done or completed; achievement: Winning the race was an *accomplishment* for the athlete. 2. A skill or ability, especially a social grace.

ad·just [ə·just'] *v.* 1. To arrange so as to fit or match. 2. To regulate for a desired result: The room was cold, so we *adjusted* the heater.

a·do·be [ə·dō'bē] *n.* 1. A brick that is dried in the sun instead of in an oven or kiln: The *adobe* bricks were made carefully of clay and dried in the sun. 2. The earth or clay of which such brick is made.

a·hí [ä·ē'] *adv.* There (Spanish).

Al·a·mo [al'ə·mō] *n.* A vacant mission building made into a fort in San Antonio, Texas, that was attacked and taken by Mexicans in 1836.

Al·bu·quer·que [al'bə·kûr'ki] *n*. A city in central New Mexico.

al·to [äl'tō] *adj.*, *adv*. High; tall; stop (Spanish).

am·bas·sa·dor [am·bas'ə·dər *or* am·bas'ə·dôr] *n*. An official of the highest rank sent to represent a government in another country: The president met with the *ambassadors* from France and Great Britain.

an·chor [ang'kər] *n*. A metal object with hooks that grip the bottom, lowered into the water by a chain or rope: The *anchor* kept the boat from drifting away.

An·glo-Sax·on [ang'glō·sak'sən] 1. *n*. A member of the Germanic people living in England who were conquered by the Normans in 1066. 2. *n*. Their language; Old English: *Anglo-Saxon* is a foreign language for today's English-speaking people.

an·noy [ə·noi'] *v*. To bother; irritate: Their loud talking *annoyed* me.

an·ten·na [an·ten'ə] *n.*, *pl*. **an·ten·nae** [an·ten'ē] One of a pair of jointed, sensitive feelers on the head of various insects, crabs, lobsters, and other animals: A butterfly has two *antennae*.

ap·er·ture [ap'ər·chər] *n*. An opening or hole: We looked into the next room through an *aperture* in the wall.

ar·ro·yo [ä·rō'yō] *n*. A brook; small stream; gutter (Spanish).

ath·lete [ath'lēt] *n*. A person with skill in sports or games that take strength, speed, or dexterity, as football, tennis, or running: Her track record proves that she is a good *athlete*.

au·to·graph [ô'tə·graf] 1. *n*. A person's name written in that person's own handwriting. 2. *v*. To write one's name on: The movie stars *autographed* their pictures.

awk·ward [ôk'wərd] *adj*. 1. Not graceful; clumsy: The long-legged colt is an *awkward* animal. 2. Embarrassing. 3. Inconvenient or hard to use.

Az·tec [az'tek] *n*. One of a nation of highly civilized Mexican Indians conquered by the Spanish under Cortés in 1521.

az·ure [azh'ər] *adj*. Sky blue: No stormy clouds crossed the *azure* sky.

Bb

bab·ble [bab'əl] 1. *v*. To make meaningless speech sounds. 2. *n*. Meaningless speech sounds: The angry crowd became a *babble* of voices.

ba·boon [ba·boon'] *n*. A large, fierce monkey of Africa and Asia, with a dog-like head and a short tail: A *baboon* is a primate, that is, one of the most advanced mammals.

back·stage [bak'stāj'] *adv*. In or toward the part of a theater behind and to the sides of the stage: The audience wanted to see the actors *backstage* in the dressing rooms.

Ba·ki·to [bä·kē′tō] Dog's name (Native American, from the Hopi language).

ban·shee [ban′shē] n. A female spirit whose wailing was supposed to warn that someone was going to die: A *banshee* was a spirit in the folklore of the Irish and Scottish Highlands.

ban·tam [ban′təm] n. A breed of small chickens, known for their fighting ability: The *bantam* is a brightly colored chicken.

bar·gain [bär′gən] n. 1. An agreement between people about something to be done or traded. 2. Something bought or offered for sale at less than its usual price: The shopper hoped to find a good *bargain* at the sale.

Bar·ri·én·tez [bä·rē·en′tes] n. A Spanish place name.

Beau·re·gard, A. Tou·tant [bō′rə·gärd, ä tōō·tan′] A business associate of Samuel Maverick.

bird·ie [bərd′ē] n. In golf, one stroke less than the standard number of strokes in which a hole should be completed: The golfer made a *birdie* on the first hole of the golf course.

bit·tern [bit′ərn] n. A long-legged bird that lives in swamps and marshes and has a harsh cry: The diet of the *bittern* is frogs, mice, lizards, and insects.

bliz·zard [bliz′ərd] n. A heavy snowstorm accompanied by strong, freezing wind: The *blizzard* stopped all traffic for several days.

bob·cat [bob′kat′] n. A wildcat of North America: A bobcat is also called a lynx.

bo·gey [bō′gē] n. In golf, one stroke over the standard number of strokes in which a hole should be completed: The golfer played more than one *bogey* and lost the golf match.

bo·lo·gna [bə·lō′nē *or* bə·lō′nə] n. A big sausage made of pork, beef, and veal: We ate *bologna* sandwiches.

bo·lo tie [bō′lō tī] n. A kind of necktie fastened with an ornamental clasp: The *bolo tie* was made of black cord and had a metal clasp.

bon·go drums [bong′gō drumz] n. A pair of joined drums held between the knees and played with the hands: They liked the fast beat of the *bongo drums*.

bound·a·ry [boun′də·rē *or* boun′drē] n. Something, as a line or mark, that forms an outer limit or edge: A river can form the *boundary* of a state or country.

Brahm [bräm] A form of Brahma, the creator of the universe in the Hindu religion.

bri·dle [brīd′(ə)l] n. The part of a harness for the head of a horse, including the bit and reins: The horse needed to be tamed to wear a *bridle*.

bub·bler [bub′(ə)lər] n. A water fountain from which water bubbles upwards: Sam drank from the *bubbler* in the park.

Bue·na Park [bwe′nä pärk] n. A suburb of Los Angeles, California.

butte [byōōt] n. A hill, standing alone, that

has steep sides and sometimes a flat top: The rain wore gulleys into the sides of the *butte*.

Cc

Ca·be·zon [cä·be·sōn'] *n*. The name of a mountain, literally *large head* (Spanish).

can·ton·ment [kan·ton'mənt] *n*. In India, a permanent military station: Once, British soldiers were housed in *cantonments* in India.

car·touche [kär· toosh'] *n*. A round or oblong figure showing a ruler's name: Ancient Egyptian tombs were decorated with *cartouches*.

cem·e·ter·y [sem'ə·ter'ē] *n*. A place where the dead are buried; a graveyard: Flowers and flags honored the dead at the *cemetery*.

Cer·van·tes, Mi·guel de [ser·vän'tes, mē· gel' de], 1547–1616, Spanish writer, author of *Don Quixote*.

chal·lenge [chal'ənj] 1. *v*. To ask for a contest, duel, or fight with: We wanted to *challenge* them to a game of tennis. 2. *n*. An invitation or dare to do something, usually difficult or dangerous. 3. *v*. To question or dispute the truth or correctness of.

Chesh·ire cat [chesh'ər *or* chesh'ir kat] *n*. A constantly grinning cat in Lewis Carroll's *Alice's Adventures in Wonderland*.

chide [chīd] *v*. **chid·ed, chid·ing** To scold: Mother *chided* me for eating so much.

chis·el [chiz'(ə)l] *n*. A cutting tool with a sharp, beveled edge, used to cut or shape wood, metal, or stone: The wood was carved with a *chisel*.

chiv·al·ry [shiv'əl·rē] *n*. The beliefs and code of life of knights in the Middle Ages: The ideal knight who practiced *chivalry* was brave, kind, and generous.

Chu·ka [choo'kä] A boy's name (Native American, from the Hopi language).

civ·il [siv'əl] *adj*. 1. Of or having to do with citizens or citizenship. 2. Courteous; polite: A *civil* question leads to a courteous answer.

civ·vies [siv'ēz] *n. pl*. Civilian clothes, to be distinguished from military uniforms: The students who wore school uniforms liked to call their play clothes *civvies*.

Cla·ri·as ba·tra·chus [clä'rē·äs' bə·trä'koos] The scientific name for a walking catfish.

club [klub] *n*. 1. A heavy wooden stick for use as a weapon. 2. A stick or bat used to hit a ball: A golfer chooses a *club* carefully. 3. A group of people organized for enjoyment or for some purpose.

clum·sy [klum'zē] *adj*. Lacking control; not graceful; awkward: Their attempts to dance were *clumsy*.

co·bra [kō'brə] *n*. A very poisonous snake of Asia and Africa that can swell its neck into a hood when excited: The word *cobra* means hooded snake.

co·co·nut [kō′kə·nut′] *n.* The large fruit of the coconut palm with a hard shell, white meat, and a center filled with sweet liquid: *Coconut* oil is used to make soap and cosmetics.

col·lapse [kə·laps′] *v.* **col·lapsed, col·laps·ing** 1. To give way; cave in. 2. To lose health or strength: After working so hard for many days, they *collapsed* from overwork.

co·lo·ni·al [kə·lō′nē·əl] *adj.* Of or living in a colony, especially the thirteen British colonies that became the U.S.: *Colonial* furniture is like the furniture used originally in the American colonies.

col·o·ny [kol′ə·nē] *n.* A group of people who live in a land separate from, but under the control of, the country from which they came: The original Massachusetts *colony* was ruled by Britain.

com·mence [kə·mens′] *v.* **com·menced, com·menc·ing** To start; begin: We *commenced* studying when the bell rang.

con·fes·sion [kən·fesh′ən] *n.* The act of making something known; admission, especially of faults or guilt: I knew they ate my pie and asked for their *confession*.

con·fuse [kən·fyōoz′] *v.* **con·fused, con·fus·ing** To mix up: The map *confused* the driver, who became lost.

con·quis·ta [kōn·kēs′tä] *n.* Conquest (Spanish).

con·so·la·tion [kon′sə·lā′shən] *n.* The act of comforting (someone) in sorrow or disappointment: When the team lost the game, the fans tried to give some *consolation*.

con·stit·u·ent [kən·stich′ōo·ənt] *n.* 1. A necessary part. 2. A voter represented by an elected official: The senator asked his *constituents* for their opinions.

con·tract [kən·trakt′] *v.* 1. To enter into a binding agreement between two or more people. 2. To draw together into a smaller space: Like a pump, the heart *contracts* and sends blood through the body.

cop·per·smith [käp′ər·smith] *n.* A tropical bird: The *coppersmith* is a bird found in India.

cow·er [kou′ər] *v.* To crouch as in fear or shame; tremble: A frightened rabbit was *cowering* under a bush.

coy·o·te [kī·ō′tē] *n.* A small wolf of the western prairies of North America: The word *coyote* comes from a Mexican Indian word for the animal.

crag [krag] *n.* A rough mass of rock jutting out from a cliff: A mountain lion was sunning himself on a *crag* high above us.

cra·ter [krā′tər] *n.* 1. A bowl-shaped hollow around an opening of a volcano. 2. A hole made by a meteorite: A lake often forms in a *crater*.

cro·quet [krō·kā′] *n.* An outdoor game in which the players use mallets with long handles to drive wooden balls through a series of wire arches: We played *croquet* on the lawn.

cure [kyŏŏr] *v.* **cured, cur·ing** 1. To restore to good health; make well. 2. To preserve meat by salting, smoking, or drying: Ham is *cured* pork.

cur·rant [kûr′ənt] *n.* 1. A small, sour, red, white, or black berry. 2. A small seedless raisin used in cooking: We put *currants* in the mincemeat pie.

Dd

dahl·ia [dal′yə] *n.* A plant that has bright, showy flowers in red, purple, yellow, or white: Some *dahlias* are shaped like balls, and others have flat petals.

Dal·las [dal′əs] *n.* A city in northeastern Texas.

de·ceive [di·sēv′] *v.* **de·ceived, de·ceiv·ing** To cause to take as true something that is not true; fool or mislead, as by lying: The clever lie is *deceiving*.

de Cor·do·va [de côr′dō·bä] A family name (Spanish).

de·lu·sion [di·lōō′zhən] *n.* A false, fixed belief, especially one held by a person who is mentally ill: The dog has the *delusion* that it is a cat.

de·scend [di·send′] *v.* 1. To go down. 2. To make a sudden attack; swoop: An eagle *descended* upon a rat.

des·sert [di·zûrt′] *n.* A sweet food, such as pie, cake, pudding, or fruit, served at the end of a **meal**: After a spicy dinner, we enjoy a sweet *dessert*.

de·ter·mi·na·tion [di·tûr′mə·nā′shən] *n.* 1. The act of deciding or settling finally. 2. Firmness of purpose; courage: Their *determination* to finish the job never faltered.

dis·patch·er [dis·pach′ər] *n.* A person who sends out scheduled trains, buses, or cars: The *dispatcher* sent a taxi to the wrong address.

dis·po·si·tion [dis′pə·zish′ən] *n.* A person's usual mood or spirit; nature; temperament: They thought their friends had kind *dispositions*.

do·be [dō′bē] *n.* Local usage of the word *adobe*. See ADOBE.

Don Qui·xo·te of La Man·cha [dŏn kē·hō′te ov lä män′chä] The hero of a Spanish novel by Cervantes. He is an idealistic but often foolish knight.

dor·mouse [dôr′mous′] *n.* A small animal that is related to the mouse but lives in trees like a squirrel: The *dormouse* is a European animal.

dou·ble [dub′əl] 1. *adj.* Twice as large, as many, or as much. 2. *n.* In baseball, a hit that enables a batter to get to second base: When the batter hit a *double* and touched second base, the fans cheered.

duch·ess [duch′is] *n.* A woman holding a rank equal to that of a duke: The *duchess* married the duke, a nobleman with the highest rank below that of a prince.

dug·out [dug′out′] *n.* A low, covered shelter at a baseball diamond, in which players sit when not on the field: We watched the batter strike out and return to the *dugout*.

Dul·ci·ne·a [dōōl·sē·ne′ä] A woman's name (Spanish).

dune [d(y)ōōn] *n.* A hill or bank of loose sand heaped up by the wind: The sand *dunes* looked like tan waves.

Ee

eel [ēl] *n.* A fish with a long, thin, snakelike body: An *eel* is about thirty inches long.

egg [eg] *v.* To urge or coax into doing something: They tried to *egg* us on to jump.

e·lim·i·nate [i·lim'ə·nāt] *v.* **e·lim·i·nat·ed, e·lim·i·nat·ing** 1. To get rid of. 2. To take out or omit. 3. To remove from competition, as by defeating: Our team lost the first game and was *eliminated* from the championship tournament.

em·per·or [em'pər·ər] *n.* A person who rules over an empire: The *emperor* ruled several nations which were all united under one government.

en·dur·ance [in·d(y)ŏŏr'əns] *n.* The ability or power to bear up or last under continued effort, hardship, or strain: The swimmer wanted to develop *endurance* for long races.

ep·i·lep·sy [ep'ə·lep'sē] *n.* A disorder of the nervous system, attacks of which sometimes cause loss of consciousness and convulsions: *Epilepsy* is sometimes called "the falling sickness."

ex·as·per·ate [ig·zas'pə·rāt] *v.* **ex·as·per·at·ed, ex·as·per·at·ing** To annoy or irritate almost to the point of anger: Their constant lateness *exasperated* us.

ex·pand [ik·spand'] *v.* 1. To make or become larger. 2. To spread out by unfolding: The peacock *expanded* its tail.

ex·traor·di·nar·y [ik·strôr'də·ner'ē *or* eks'trə·ôr'də·ner'ē] *adj.* Remarkable; unusual; surprising: The small animal's strength was *extraordinary*.

eye·tooth [ī'tōōth'] *n.* An upper tooth near the front of the mouth: Each of the *eyeteeth* is the third tooth from the middle on either side.

Ff

Fahr·en·heit [far'ən·hīt] *adj.* Of or indicating the temperature scale used for ordinary purposes in the U.S. and Great Britain. In this system water freezes at 32 degrees and boils at 212 degrees.

fate [fāt] *n.* 1. A power supposed to determine the way things happen. 2. What happens to a person: It was their *fate* to lose the game.

Fe·li·ces Pas·cuas [fe·lē'ses päs'kwäs] Happy Christmas (Spanish).

fib [fib] 1. *n.* A lie told without bad intention about something unimportant: The children told a *fib* about how many cookies they had eaten. 2. *v.* To tell a fib.

filth·y [fil'thē] *adv.* Dirty; covered with filth: After they played in the mud, their clothes were *filthy*.

flock [flok] 1. *n.* A group of animals of the same kind herded, feeding, or moving together. 2. *n.* A large number or group. 3. *v.* To come or move together in a crowd: On hot days, people *flocked* to the beach.

fore·cast [fôr'kast'] 1. *v.* To predict after studying available facts. 2. *n.* A prediction, as of coming weather conditions: We listen to the weather *forecast* every morning.

frail [frā(ə)l] *adj.* Easily damaged in body or structure; weak: The *frail*, old dog could barely walk.

Fran·cis·ca [frän·sēs'kä] A woman's name (Spanish).

freight [frāt] *n*. 1. The service of shipping goods by train, truck, ship, or plane at regular rates. 2. Goods shipped in this way: That train carries *freight*, not passengers.

fron·tier [frun·tir′] *n*. 1. The border of a country. 2. The border of settled land; the beginning of the wilderness: In 1850, land west of the Mississippi River was the American *frontier*.

frus·trate [frus′trāt] *v*. **frus·trat·ed, frus·trat·ing** To hinder the efforts of or bring to nothing: The long delay *frustrated* them.

Gg

ga·la [gā′lə] *n*. A lively celebration; festival: Many people were invited to a *gala* to honor her birthday.

Gar·ci·a [gär·cē′ä] A family name (Spanish).

gath·er [gath′ər] *v*. 1. To bring together or come together: People *gathered* to hear the candidate's speech. 2. To draw cloth into folds.

gland [gland] *n*. Any of several organs of the body that have to do with the production, storage, or secretion of certain substances, either for elimination as waste or for use elsewhere in the body: The liver is a *gland*.

gnaw [nô] *v*. To bite or eat away little by little: The dog *gnawed* on its bone.

good-tem·pered [good′tem′pərd] *adj*. Having a kind, even disposition or character: The dog was *good-tempered* and never bit anyone.

gran·deur [gran′jər] *n*. Largeness and splendor: The *grandeur* of the palace amazed visitors.

grav·i·ty [grav′ə·tē] *n*. The force by which any two bodies attract each other, as shown by the tendency of objects to fall toward the center of the earth: Without *gravity*, people would be weightless.

Gua·na·jua·to [gwä·nä·hwä′tō] *n*. 1. A state in Mexico, lying in a mountainous region in central Mexico. 2. The capital of the state of Guanajuato.

guff [guf] *n*. Nonsense: Full of *guff*, they tended to exaggerate their activities and annoy their friends.

guide [gīd] 1. *v*. To show the way to; lead: Someone will *guide* us through the cave so we don't become lost. 2. *n*. A person who conducts or leads others, as on a trip or tour.

gur·ney [gûr′nē] *n*. A cot on wheels; stretcher: The patient was taken to the hospital room on a *gurney*.

Hh

hand·i·cap [han′dē·kap] *n*. Any disadvantage; something that makes success difficult: A poor education can be a *handicap*.

Hanh [hahnkh] *adv*. Yes (Native American, from the Dakota language).

hare [hâr] *n*. A shy, rabbitlike animal having a split upper lip: The *hare* is noted for its speed.

hat·ter [hat′ər] *n*. A person who makes or deals in hats: The *hatter* sold many unusual hats in his shop.

Hau [hah′oo] *interj*. A greeting (Native American, from the Hopi language).

heave [hēv] *v*. 1. To lift or throw with great effort. 2. To breathe hard; pant. 3. To expand and contract rhythmically: The sailor liked to watch the waves *heave* against the dock.

Henry II [hen′rē], 1519–1559, king of France from 1547 to 1559.

hi·er·o·glyphs [hī′ər·ə·glifs′] *n. pl.* Pictures or symbols representing objects, ideas, or sounds: The ancient Egyptians used *hiero-glyphs*.

Hin·du [hin′dōō] *n.* 1. A native of India descended from an ancient race that conquered it. 2. A person whose religion is Hinduism.

hinh [hēnkh] *interj.* A sigh (Native American, from the Hopi language).

Hit·ler [hit′lər], Adolf, 1889–1945, leader of Nazi Germany from 1933 to 1945.

hoist [hoist] 1. *v.* To raise or lift, especially by mechanical means: We *hoisted* the hay into the loft. 2. *n.* A machine that hoists. 3. *n.* A lift or boost.

Hok·si·las [hohk·shē′lahs] *n.* Boys (Native American, from the Dakota language).

hom·bre [ōm′bre] *n.* Man (Spanish).

ho·mog·en·ize [hə·moj′ə·nīz] *v.* **ho·mog·en·ized, ho·mog·en·iz·ing** To mix the cream throughout the milk so that it cannot separate: The milk we bought at the store was *homogenized* and pasteurized.

Ho·pi [hō′pē] *n.* A member of a tribe of Indians now living in towns built of stone in northeastern Arizona.

hum·ming·bird [hum′ing·bûrd′] *n.* A tiny, brightly colored bird with a long bill: The *hummingbird* moves its wings so rapidly that they hum.

hutch [huch] *n.* 1. A pen or coop for keep-ing small animals: The rabbits lived in a *hutch*. 2. A chest, box, or cupboard used for storage.

hys·ter·i·cal [his·ter′ə·kəl] *adj.* Showing un-controlled excitement or emotion: After the car accident, the driver became *hysterical*.

Ii

im·i·tate [im′ə·tāt] *v.* To try to act or look the same way: Children sometimes *imitate* their parents.—**im′i·ta′tion** *n.*

im·me·di·ate [i·mē′dē·it] *adj.* Done or hap-pening without delay; at once: The wound needed *immediate* care.

in·de·cent [in·dē′sənt] *adj.* Not proper or decent: Criticism of the king was considered *indecent* by some citizens.

in·ning [in′ing] *n.* A part of a baseball game during which each team has a turn at bat until it makes three outs: A regular baseball game has nine *innings*.

in·spi·ra·tion [in′spə·rā′shən] *n.* 1. A good idea or impulse that comes to someone, usually suddenly. 2. A person or thing that arouses a feeling or idea in someone: That person's life is an *inspiration* to others.—**in′spi·ra′tion·al** *adj.*

in·vade [in·vād′] *v.* 1. To enter by force with the purpose of conquering. 2. To rush or swarm into; overrun: Weeds began to *invade* the garden.—**in·va′sion** *n.*

ir·rev·o·ca·ble [i·rev′ə·kə·bəl] *adj.* Incapa-ble of being brought back, undone, or changed: Their decision to quit their jobs was *irrevocable*.

Jj

jack·knife [jak′nīf′] *n., v.* **jack·knifed,**

jack·knif·ing 1. *n.* A large knife with folding blades, carried in the pocket. 2. *v.* To double up like a jackknife, as a tractor and trailer that are hitched together: When the driver slammed on the brakes, the truck *jackknifed*.

jeop·ar·dy [jep′ər·dē] *n.* Danger of death, loss, or injury: Poor brakes on the car put the driver in *jeopardy*.

jerk [jûrk] *v.* To give a sharp, sudden pull or twist to; pull or tug at: He began to *jerk* the weeds out of the garden.

jock·ey [jok′ē] *n.* A person employed to ride horses in races: The *jockey* was short and thin, so the horse had a light load and ran faster.

jour·ney [jûr′nē] 1. *n.* Travel from one place to another; trip: Our *journey* by train lasted three days. 2. *v.* To make a trip; travel.

Kk

kan·ga·roo [kang′gə·roo′] *n.* An Australian animal that has short, weak forelegs, strong hind legs used for leaping, and a long thick tail: The female *kangaroo* has a pouch in which it carries its young.

ker·o·sene [ker′ə·sēn] *n.* A thin oil made from petroleum: *Kerosene* is used for a fuel in lamps and stoves.

king·dom [king′dəm] *n.* 1. A country ruled by a king or queen: The *kingdom* was ruled by a king and queen. 2. An area or sphere where someone or something is dominant.

knave [nāv] *n.* 1. A sly, dishonest person. 2. The jack, a playing card: The three face cards in a deck of cards are the king, queen, and *knave*.

knight [nīt] *n.* In the Middle Ages, a mounted warrior who vowed to do good deeds and serve his king: In the Middle Ages, a *knight* who traveled in search of adventure was called a knight-errant.

Ll

lab·o·ra·to·ry [lab′rə·tôr′ē] *n.* A building or room equipped for doing scientific work or experiments: They found test tubes and chemicals in the *laboratory*.

la·ma [lä′mə] *n.* A Buddhist priest or monk: A *lama* is a priest of Buddha, a religious leader of India.

lance [lans] *n.* A long weapon with a sharp metal head: A knight usually carried a *lance*.

lan·guid [lang′gwid] *adj.* Lacking energy or spirit; weak: The summer heat often makes them feel *languid*.

La Pal·ma [lä päl′mä] *n.* A city in southern California.

Las Cru·ces [läs kroo′ses] *n.* A city on the Rio Grande in south-central New Mexico.

Le·Maire, E·ti·enne [lə·mâr′, ā′tē·in′] A Frenchman who was the steward of Thomas Jefferson.

lig·a·ment [lig′ə·mənt] *n.* A band of firm, strong tissue that connects bones or helps to support an organ of the body: The word *ligament* comes from a Latin word meaning to tie.

loom [loom] *n.* A machine on which thread or yarn is woven into cloth: Rugs can be woven on a *loom*.

Mm

mag·pie [mag′pī] *n*. Any of various large, noisy birds, having a long tapering tail and black and white plumage: A *magpie* belongs to the same family of birds as crows and eats almost all kinds of food.

mam·moth [mam′ əth] *n*. A large, now extinct animal related to the elephant: The *mammoth* had long tusks and hairy skin.

mar·a·thon [mar′ə·thon] *n*. A foot race of twenty-six miles, 385 yards, so called from a messenger's run from the plain of Marathon to Athens, Greece, to announce the victory of the Greeks over the Persians: The *marathon* is a feature of the Olympic Games.

ma·rine [mə·rēn′] 1. *adj*. Of, having to do with, formed by, or found in the sea. 2. *n*. A member of the service within the U.S. Navy Department which has combat troops and air forces: They were *marines* in the U.S. Marine Corps.

ma·son·ry [mā′sən·rē] *n*. A thing of stone or brick built by a mason: The front of the building was granite *masonry*.

Ma·ta·gor·do Pen·in·su·la [mä·tä·gôr′dä pə·nin′s(y)ə·lə] *n*. A peninsula in southeastern Texas, between Galveston and Corpus Christi.

may·or [mā′ər] *n*. The chief governing official of a city or town: The citizens elected a new *mayor* for their town.

me·chan·i·cal [mə·kan′i·kəl] *adj*. Of or having to do with a machine: *Mechanical* engineers created new tools.

Me·di·ci [meh′dē·chē], **Catherine de,** 1519–1589, the wife of Henry II of France and the daughter of Lorenzo, Duke of Urbino, of the famous Medici family of Florence, Italy.

mon·goose [mong′ gōos] *n*. A small animal of Asia and Africa: The *mongoose* preys on snakes and rats.

monk [mungk] *n*. One who is a member of a religious order and lives apart from other people, but usually among other monks: The *monk* promised to obey the rules of the religious order.

Mon·ti·cel·lo [mon′tə·sel′ō] *n*. The home of Thomas Jefferson, in central Virginia, near Charlottesville.

mus·cle [mus′əl] *n*. One of the bundles of tissue in the body that, by contracting and stretching, produce the body's movements: The word *muscle* comes from a Latin word meaning a little mouse, because a bunched muscle can look like a little mouse.

musk·rat [musk′rat] *n*. A mammal with glossy, brown fur and a strong scent: The *muskrat* belongs to the animal family which includes mice, rats, squirrels, and beavers.

Nn

Na·po·le·on [nə·pō′lē·ən], 1769–1821, French military leader and conqueror, emperor of France from 1804 to 1815.

Neb·khep·er·u·ra [neb·khep′ûr·o͞o·rä′] The royal name of Tutankhamun.

Ne·ro [nir′ō], 37–68, emperor of Rome from 54 to 68.

Oo

O·ki·na·wa [ō′kə·nä′wə] *n.* 1. An island group which is part of Japan. 2. One island in the group.

O·ri·ent [ôr′ē·ənt] *n.* The countries east of Europe; Asia, especially eastern Asia: *Orient* comes from a Latin word meaning rising, because the sun rises in the east. —**O′ri·en·tal** *adj.*

or·na·ment [ôr′nə·mənt] *n.* Something that makes another thing more beautiful; a decoration: The beautiful clock was the room's only *ornament*.

oys·ter [ois′tər] *n.* A shellfish having a soft body within a rough, irregularly-shaped shell in two parts hinged together: Some *oysters* are good to eat and some form pearls.

Pp

par [pär] *n.* In golf, a standard number of strokes in which a hole or course should be completed: The golfers were happy when they completed the course under *par*.

par·a·chute [par′ə·sho͞ot] *n.* A large, expanding, umbrella-shaped object that slows the speed, especially in falling, of a thing or person to which it is attached: A *parachute* was used to drop supplies from the airplane.

pass [pas] 1. *v.* To move past or go by: The hour *passed* slowly as we waited for the party. 2. *n.* The throwing or hitting of a ball from a player to a teammate.

pas·teur·ize [pas′chə·rīz] *v.* **pas·teur·ized, pas·teur·iz·ing** To heat from 140° to 155° F. in order to destroy bacteria: The word *pasteurize* comes from the name of Louis Pasteur, who discovered that bacteria were carried in the air and caused diseases.

perch [pûrch] 1. *n.* A pole, branch, or bar used as a roost for birds. 2. *v.* To sit or place on or as on a perch: The painter was *perched* on a ladder.

per·il·ous [per′əl·əs] *adj.* Risky; dangerous: Mountain climbing can be a *perilous* sport.

per·ma·nent [pûr′mən·ənt] *adj.* Continuing or intended to continue without change; lasting; enduring; durable: They disliked moving frequently and wanted a *permanent* home.

per·sim·mon [pər·sim′ən] *n.* A North American tree that bears reddish, plumlike fruit: *Persimmon* is sweet to eat when the fruit is ripe.

pe·ti·tion [pə·tish′ən] *n.* A formal, written request, often with many signatures, sent to a person or group in authority: The neighbors signed a *petition* asking for a crossing guard at the busy street corner.

Pi·ne·da, Al·va·ro [pē·ne′dä, äl′vä·rō], 1945-1975, A famous jockey who won the George Woolf Memorial Award in 1974 for riding the most winning horses of the season.

pipe [pīp] *n., v.* **piped, pip·ing** 1. *n.* A long tube for carrying water, oil, gas, or steam from one place to another. 2. *v.* To speak or sing in a shrill, high-pitched tone: We heard a bird *piping* to its companions.

plat·y·pus [plat′ə·pəs] *n.* A small, egg-laying water mammal of Australia, having a ducklike bill, webbed feet, and a broad, flat tail: The average *platypus* is twenty inches long.

pneu·mo·nia [n(y)ōō·mōn′yə] *n.* A disease marked by the swelling of one or both lungs: His cold led to a more serious disease, *pneumonia*.

Po·lo [pō′lō], **Mar·co**, 1254?–1324?, a traveler from Venice, Italy, who wrote about his travels to Asia.

pope [pōp] *n.* The bishop of Rome, head of the Roman Catholic Church: The *pope* is elected by Church officials.

Port Hue·ne·me [pôrt wī′nē·mē *or* wä·nē′mē] *n.* A city in southern California, between Santa Barbara and Los Angeles.

pos·i·tron [päz′ə·trän′] *n.* An atomic particle having a positive charge; a positive electron: *Positrons* were first discovered in cosmic rays. —**pos′i·tron′ic** *adj.*

pro·jec·tive [prə·jek′tiv] *adj.* Extending forward or jutting out: Extending out from the house, the bay window was *projective*.

prompt [prompt] *adj.* Ready; quick; on time: They wanted to be *prompt* and watched the time carefully. —**prompt′·ly** *adv.*

pro·tec·tion [prə·tek′shən] *n.* A person or thing that guards (someone) from attack, harm, or injury: Locks are a *protection* against theft.

prov·i·dence [prov′ə·dəns] *n.* The care and protection of a supernatural being or nature: Only *providence* kept us from being drowned.

pu·ri·fy [pyŏŏr′ə·fī] *v.* **pu·ri·fied, pu·ri·fy·ing** To make or become clean or good: Smog settled over the city and citizens waited for a *purifying* thunderstorm.

Qq

qua·ver [kwā′vər] *v.* To tremble or shake in an uncertain way: We knew they were scared because their voices were *quavering*.

Rr

ra·dar [rā′där] *n.* A device for locating objects and learning their size and speed by sending out radio waves: The word *radar* comes from ra(dio) d(etection) a(nd) r(anging).

rad·ish [rad′ish] *n.* A small, crisp, sharp-tasting plant root, eaten raw: A *radish* has a red or white skin.

rai·sin [rā′zən] *n.* A sweet grape of a special sort dried in the sun or in an oven: For breakfast we ate cereal with *raisins* in it.

ran·cho [rän′chō] *n.* A ranch; small farm (Spanish).

reck·on [rek′ən] *v. informal* To suppose: I didn't see them today, so I *reckon* they are busy.

reins [rānz] *n. pl.* Straps attached to the bit to control a horse or other animal which is being ridden or driven: We pulled the horse's *reins* when we wanted to stop.

re·lax [ri·laks′] *v.* 1. To avoid work or exercise; rest. 2. To make or become less tight or firm: Tired muscles *relax* in a hot bath.

rel·ic [rel'ik] *n.* Something remaining from what has disappeared or been destroyed: The vase is a *relic* of ancient Greece.

res·er·va·tion [rez'ər·vā'shən] *n.* 1. The act of holding back or setting aside something. 2. A doubt or possible objection. 3. A tract of government land set aside for a special purpose: The United States government once set up Indian *reservations*.

re·sist [ri·zist'] *v.* 1. To withstand. 2. To keep from: They can't *resist* television.

re·trac·tive [ri·trak'tiv] *adj.* Capable of drawing back or in: The seat belts of most cars are *retractive*.

rig [rig] 1. *v.* To fit a ship with sails and other gear. 2. *n. U. S. informal* A large truck: The driver was proud of his shiny diesel *rig*.

ring [ring] 1. *n.* A circle or round loop: Saturn is a planet surrounded by *rings*. 2. *n.* A narrow circle of metal or other material worn on a finger as an ornament. 3. *v.* To form a circle: Flowering plants *ringed* the tree.

Ri·o Gran·de Riv·er [rē'ō grän'de riv'ər] *n.* A river in the Southwest U.S., forming part of the border with Mexico.

Ri·o Puer·co [rē'ō pwer'kō] *n.* The muddy or dirty river (Spanish).

Ro·dri·guez [rō·drē'ges] A family name (Spanish).

Ro·si·nan·te [rō·sē·nän'te] The name of Don Quixote's horse (Spanish).

run [run] 1. *v.* To move or go along by using steps that are faster than walking steps. 2. *n.* In baseball, a score made by a player's running around and touching all bases: The

player crossed home plate and gave the team its first *run*.

Ss

Sac·a·ja·we·a [säc'ä·jä·wē'ä], 1787?–1812?, the interpreter for the Lewis and Clark Expedition to the Pacific Ocean.

sal·a·man·der [sal'ə·man'dər] *n.* A small lizardlike animal related to the frog, having a smooth, moist skin: *Salamanders* live in damp places.

sa·li·va [sə·lī'və] *n.* The liquid produced in the mouth; spit: *Saliva* helps prepare food for digestion.

San·cho Pan·za [sän'chō pän'zä] The servant of Don Quixote.

sav·age [sav'ij] *adj.* Wild, untamed, and often fierce: Many people think a lion is a *savage* beast. —**sav'age·ly** *adv.*

scar·ab [skar'əb] *n.* 1. A large black beetle considered sacred by the ancient Egyptians. 2. A charm or ornament representing this beetle: An ivory *scarab* hung from the bracelet.

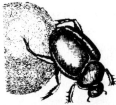

scorn·ful [skôrn'fəl] *adj.* Full of a feeling of disliking someone or something as low or beneath one's notice: The bulldog looked at the mutt with a *scornful* glance. —**scorn'ful·ly** *adv.*

scout [skout] *n.* Someone sent out to find out about a rival or an area of land: Explorers send *scouts* ahead to find campsites and locate dangers.

scrump·tious [skrum(p)'shəs] *adj.* *slang* Nice; very fine; delightful: They ate all of the *scrumptious* cake.

sei·zure [sē'zhər] *n.* 1. The act of taking hold of suddenly and with force. 2. A sudden, violent attack, as of a disease: The patient had a *seizure* of coughing.

sen·si·ble [sen'sə·bəl] *adj.* Having or showing wisdom or good judgment: The child was *sensible* and knew what to do in an emergency.

ser·pent [sûr'pənt] *n.* A snake, especially a large one: A python is a *serpent* about thirteen feet long.

Se·ville [sə·vil'] *n.* A city in southwestern Spain.

shaft [shaft] *n.* 1. The long, narrow rod of an arrow or spear. 2. A deep passage sunk into the earth: We entered the underground mine through the *shaft*.

sheep·ish [shē'pish] *adj.* Foolish, meek, or shy: After spilling the milk, Terry looked *sheepish.*—**sheep'ish·ly** *adv.*

sher·bet [shûr'bit] *n.* A frozen dessert made with water, milk, sugar, and fruit juice: The word *sherbet* comes from an Arabic word meaning drink.

shrug [shrug] *v.* To draw up the shoulders to show doubt, dislike, or indifference: When they don't care, they just *shrug*.

sieve [siv] *n.* A utensil with holes in the bottom, used to separate solids too large to pass through from fine pieces or a liquid: The fine gold was mixed with larger stones, so the miner used a *sieve* to remove the gold.

sift [sift] *v.* To pass through a sieve or strainer in order to separate the fine parts from the coarse: We *sifted* the sand to get rid of pebbles.

sig·na·ture [sig'nə·chər] *n.* The name of a person written by himself: People must write their *signatures* on their bank checks.

Sioux [sōō] *n.* A member of a group of Indian tribes of the north central U.S.

slack·en [slak'ən] *v.* 1. To make or become less tight or firm; loosen. 2. To make or become slower, less active, or less forceful: The children were frustrated by the poor directions and began to *slacken* their efforts.

slime [slīm] *n.* Any soft, moist, sticky substance that clings and often soils: The bottom of the lake was covered with *slime*.

sluice [slōōs] *n.* An artificial channel for conducting water: Water flowed through an open *sluice* in the dam.

spi·ral [spī'rəl] 1. *n.* A curve traced by a point that moves around a fixed center from which its distance continuously increases or decreases. 2. *n.* A curve resembling the thread of a screw. 3. *adj.* Winding or curving like a spiral: Laura stood on the fourth floor at the top of a *spiral* staircase and watched the people below on the first floor.

spoil [spoil] *v.* **spoiled** *or* **spoilt, spoil·ing,** *n.* 1. *v.* To become damaged or rotten, as food. 2. *v.* To weaken or destroy the character of a child by giving in to the child's demands too often: The parents *spoiled* their children by buying many toys for them. 3. *n. pl.* Things taken over by force: Their enemies gathered the *spoils* of war.

squire [skwīr] *n.* A young man who served as an attendant to a knight: The *squire* followed his knight into battle.

state·ly [stāt′lē] *adj.* Dignified; impressive: The prince bowed in a *stately* manner.

stilt [stilt] *n.* One of a pair of long, slender poles made with a projection to support the foot some distance above the ground in walking: That tall, stiff figure is only Fred walking on *stilts*.

stir·rup [stûr′əp *or* stir′əp] *n.* One of a pair of loops with flattened bases suspended by straps on each side of a saddle to support a rider's foot: *Stirrups* are made of wood, metal, or leather.

stow·a·way [stō′ə·wā′] *n.* A person who hides aboard a ship or train to travel without buying a ticket: The conductor found a *stowaway* on the train.

strand [strand] *v.* 1. To drive or run aground, as a ship. 2. To leave behind or in a helpless position: After their car broke down, they were *stranded* in a strange city.

sub·way [sub′wā] *n.* An electric railroad that

is mainly underground: We rode on the *subway* in New York City.

Su·mi·ko [soo̅·mē′kō] A woman's name (Japanese).

sun·dae [sun′dē] *n.* A dish of ice cream topped with crushed fruit, syrup, and nuts: I had a chocolate *sundae* with a cherry and nuts.

swal·low [swol′ō] *v.* To make the muscular action that causes food or liquid to pass from the mouth into the stomach: When someone has a sore throat, food is hard to *swallow*.

sym·pa·thy [sim′pə·thē] *n.* The condition of being affected by another's feelings or situations: Our *sympathy* was given to the man in pain.

Tt

Ta·ko·za [tah·koh′zhah] *n.* Grandchild (a form of *Takozakpaku*, Native American, from the Dakota language).

tal·low [tal′ō] *n.* The fat of certain animals, as of cows or sheep: Some candles are made from tallow.

tank·er [tangk′ər] *n.* A truck built to carry liquids, especially oil: A *tanker* delivered gasoline to the gas station.

ten·der [ten′dər] *adj.* 1. Easily injured or damaged; delicate; sensitive. 2. Kind and gentle; loving: They gave the kittens *tender* care.—**ten′der·ly** *adv.*

ten·don [ten′dən] *n.*
A tough band of tissue
that connects a muscle
to a bone: The word
tendon comes from a
Latin word meaning to
stretch.

te·pee [tē′pē] *n.* A
cone-shaped tent used
by some North Ameri-
can Indians: *Tepee*
comes from two Indian
words meaning *used
for dwelling.*

ter·mi·nal [tûr′mə·nəl] 1. *adj.* Of, at, or
having to do with, or forming a limit or end.
2. *n.* The station at the end of a railway or
bus route: Passengers waited at the bus *ter-
minal.*

ter·race [ter′is] *n.* 1.
A raised, level space,
as of lawn, with one or
more sloping sides:
The hillside was made
into *terraces* so that
the farmers could
plant crops more eas-
ily. 2. A paved area
adjoining a house; pa-
tio.

ter·rain [tə·rān′] *n.* An area or tract of land:
The *terrain* around the camp was rocky.

ter·rif·ic [tə·rif′ik] *adj.* 1. *informal* Wonderful; splendid: They thought the book was *terrific* and read it several times. 2. *informal*
Extreme or very great. 3. Causing great ter-
ror or fear.

Thai·land [tī′land] *n.* A country in southeastern Asia.

The·o·phi·lus [thē′o′phə·ləs] A name of
Greek origin.

thun·der·bolt [thun′dər·bōlt] *n.* 1. A flash
of lightning together with a clap of thunder:
Thunderbolts warned us of an advancing
storm. 2. Something very shocking and
sudden.

tide [tīd] *n.* The rise and fall of the surface
of the ocean or of waters joined with an
ocean, caused by the attraction of the sun
and moon: The *tide* rises and falls twice
daily, or about every twelve hours.

To·bo·so [tō·bō′sō] *n.* A Spanish place
name.

ton·sil [ton′səl] *n.* One of two oval masses of
soft glandular tissue, one on each side of the
throat at the back of the mouth: Scientists
think that *tonsils* help destroy harmful bacteria.

ton·sil·lec·to·my [ton′sə·lek′tə·mē] *n.* A
surgical operation in which the tonsils are
removed: The doctor performed a *tonsillectomy* at the hospital.

tour·na·ment [tŏŏr′nə·ment *or* tûr′nə·mənt]
n. A series of matches in a sport or game
involving many players: We played in a
championship tennis *tournament.*

tram·ple [tram′pəl] *v.* **tram·pled, tram·
pling** To walk or stamp on heavily, especially so as to crush or hurt: The runaway
horse was *trampling* the garden.

tra·peze [trə·pēz′] *n.*
A short swinging bar,
suspended by two
ropes: The circus per-
former was swinging
above us on a *tra-
peze.*

tread [tred] *v.* 1. To step or walk in, over,

along. 2. In swimming, to keep the body erect and the head above water by moving the feet up and down as if walking: The beginning swimmer wanted to learn how to *tread* water.

tum·ble [tum′bəl] *v.* **tum·bled, tum·bling** To perform acrobatics, such as somersaults: *Tumbling* demands quick, easy grace.

tusk [tusk] *n.* One of the two very large teeth that stick out of the mouths of animals such as the elephant and the walrus: The elephant uses its *tusks* to protect itself.

Tut·ankh·a·mun [to͞ot′ängk·ä′min], 14th century B.C., king of Egypt, whose tomb was discovered in 1922.

ty·rant [tī′rənt] *n.* A ruler having complete power: Most people think a *tyrant* is one who rules cruelly and unfairly.

Uu

un·con·scious [un·kon′shəs] *adj.* Not able to feel and think; not conscious: He was *unconscious* during the operation.

ur·gent [ûr′ jənt] *adj.* Needing or demanding quick action: Victims of the flood had an *urgent* need for food.

ush·er [ush′ər] *n.* A person who conducts people to their seats, as in a theater: The *usher* looked at our tickets and showed us our seats.

Vv

va·cant [vā′kənt] *adj.* 1. Empty, unfilled, or unused. 2. Being or appearing to be without thought, intelligence, or interest: The sleepy person stared and wore a *vacant* look on his face.

ven·ti·la·tor [ven′tə·lā′tər] *n.* A device or opening for changing the air, as in a room: A *ventilator* allowed hot air to escape from the engine room.

ve·ran·da [və·ran′də] *n.* A long, open, outdoor porch, usually roofed, along the outside of a building: A *veranda* continued along two sides of the old hotel.

ver·dict [vûr′dikt] *n.* The decision of a jury after a trial: The jury tried to reach a *verdict*.

vul·ture [vul′chər] *n.* A large bird, usually with a naked head, that feeds mostly on decaying flesh: The *vulture* is related to the hawk and eagle.

Ww

Wa·kan·tan·ka [wah·kahnk′tahnk·ka] *n.* Great Spirit (Native American, from the Dakota language).

ward [wôrd] *n.* A large room in a hospital, usually equipped to care for six or more patients: The patient was moved from a private room to a *ward*.

wave [wāv] 1. *v.* To move or cause to move back and forth. 2. *n.* The motion or pulse that carries energy: Sound reaches our ears as *waves*, and light reaches our eyes as *waves*.

wave·length [wāv′leng(k)th′] *n*. The distance between parts of waves: A high-pitched sound has shorter *wavelengths* than a low-pitched sound.

weak·ness [wēk′nis] *n*. 1. The condition of lacking strength or ability. 2. A fault or flaw: That person's only *weakness* is a tendency to be tardy.

wea·sel [wē′zəl] *n*. A small, slender animal with brownish fur that preys on smaller animals and birds: The *weasel* eats mice and rats.

weird [wird] *adj*. 1. Strange in an unearthly or supernatural way. 2. *informal* Peculiar; odd: They wore *weird* neckties.

Wi·cin·ca·la [wē·chēnk′chah·lah] *n*. Girl (Native American, from the Dakota language).

Wi·ki [wē′kē] Chuka's hawk's name (Native American, from the Hopi language).

wrasse [ras] *n*. Any of several long, brightly colored marine fish with spiny fins: One kind of blue-striped *wrasse* found in the Mediterranean Sea is called a peacock fish.

Yy

Ya·ma·da [yä·mä′dä] A family name (Japanese).

yip·py [yi′pē] *adj*. Barking sharply: The *yippy* little dog was afraid of the strangers.

Zz

zip·per [zip′ər] *n*. A fastener having two rows of interlocking teeth that may be joined by a sliding device: The front of the jacket was held together with a *zipper*.

ACKNOWLEDGMENTS

For permission to adapt and reprint copyrighted materials, grateful acknowledgment is made to the following publishers, authors, and other copyright holders:

Isaac Asimov, author, and *Boys' Life*, for "A Boy's Best Friend" by Isaac Asimov, reprinted by permission of the author and *Boys' Life*, published by the Boy Scouts of America.

Evelyn M. Begley, author, for permission to adapt her previously unpublished articles "Lee Trevino" and "Alvaro Pineda — Jockey."

Bill Cosby, author, for "Tonsils," copyright © 1966 by William H. Cosby, Jr., adapted by permission.

Coward, McCann & Geoghegan, Inc., for "Muscles Make You Move" by Edith Lucie Weart, adaptation by permission of Coward, McCann & Geoghegan, Inc., from *The Story of Your Bones* by Edith Weart, copyright © 1966 by Edith Lucie Weart; Coward, McCann & Geoghegan, Inc., and McIntosh and Otis, Inc., for "Big Rig" by Bill and Rosalie Brown, adaptation by permission of Coward, McCann & Geoghegan, Inc., from *Big Rig* by Bill and Rosalie Brown, copyright © 1959 by Bill and Rosalie Brown, reprinted by permission of McIntosh and Otis, Inc.

The Curtis Publishing Company, for "Chuka's Hawk" by Elizabeth B. Whitmore, from *Jack and Jill* magazine, copyright © 1964 by The Curtis Publishing Company.

E. P. Dutton & Company, Inc., and The Bodley Head, for "Otherwise Known As Sheila the Great" by Judy Blume, from *Otherwise Known as Sheila the Great* by Judy Blume, copyright © 1972 by Judy Blume, reprinted by permission of the publishers, E. P. Dutton, and The Bodley Head.

Family Weekly, for "Patty Wilson's Magnificent Marathon" by Sheila Cragg, reprinted by permission of *Family Weekly*, copyright © 1978, 641 Lexington Avenue, New York, New York 10022.

Farrar, Straus & Giroux, Inc., and McIntosh and Otis, Inc., for "Pitcher" by Stephen Cole, a selection from *Pitcher and I* by Stephen Cole, copyright © 1946, 1947, 1963 by Stephen Cole, copyright 1946 by The Curtis Publishing Company, copyright renewed 1974, 1975 by Stephen Cole, reprinted with the permission of Farrar, Straus & Giroux, Inc., and McIntosh and Otis, Inc.

Fleet Press Corporation, for "Zip 'Er Up" by Hannah Campbell, adapted from *Why Did They Name It . . . ?* by Hannah Campbell, copyright © 1964, Fleet Press Corporation, New York.

Free To Be Foundation, Inc., for "The Southpaw" by Judith Viorst, from *Free to Be . . . You and Me*, published by McGraw-Hill, copyright © 1974 Free To Be Foundation, Inc.

Harcourt Brace Jovanovich, Inc., for "Phizzog" by Carl Sandburg, from *Good Morning, America*, copyright 1928, 1956 by Carl Sandburg, and "To Look at Any Thing" by John Moffitt, © 1961 by John Moffitt, reprinted from his volume *The Living Seed*, both reprinted by permission of Harcourt Brace Jovanovich, Inc.; Harcourt Brace Jovanovich, Inc., and Granada Publishing Limited, for "maggie and milly and molly and may" by E. E. Cummings, © 1956 by E. E. Cummings, reprinted from his volume *Complete Poems 1913-1962* by permission of Harcourt Brace Jovanovich, Inc., and Granada Publishing Limited, publishers.

Harper & Row, Publishers, Inc., for "Some Idioms" by Charles Earle Funk, from *Heavens to Betsy!* (hardbound edition) by Charles Earle Funk, adaptation of "to pull up stakes" (page 104), "to start from scratch" (page 109), and "off one's base" (page 121), copyright © 1955 by Charles Earle Funk, by permission of Harper & Row, Publishers, Inc.; Harper & Row, Publishers, Inc., The Estate of the late Louise Fitzhugh, and Victor Gollancz, Ltd., for "Harriet the Spy," adaptation of chapters 10 and 11 from *Harriet the Spy* by Louise Fitzhugh, copyright © 1964 by Louise Fitzhugh, by permission of Harper & Row, Publishers, Inc., The Estate of the late Louise Fitzhugh, and Victor Gollancz, Ltd.

Hart Publishing Company, Inc., for "I Am a Flock of Birds" by Meg Wilson, from *My Sister Looks Like a Pear: Awakening the Poetry in Young People* by Douglas Anderson, copyright 1974 Hart Publishing Company, Inc.

Texas Folklore Society, for "Tough Hombres, Tougher Pudding" by James Emmit McCauley, from *A Stove-Up Cowboy's Story* by James Emmit McCauley, by permission of the Texas Folklore Society.

The Viking Press, Inc., for "Fox at Midnight" by Betsy Byars, from *The Midnight Fox* by Betsy Byars, copyright © 1968 by Betsy Byars, reprinted by permission of The Viking Press.

Franklin Watts, Inc., for "City Hall" by Nellie Burchardt, adapted from *Project Cat* by Nellie Burchardt, copyright © 1966 by Franklin Watts, Inc., used by permission of the publisher.

West Southwest Book Publishing Company, for "Samuel A. Maverick" by Irwin and Kathryn Sexton, adapted from *Samuel A. Maverick* by Irwin and Kathryn Sexton, copyright © 1964 by The Naylor Company, used by permission of West Southwest Book Publishing Company of Redding, California.

The story "Cabezon" appeared originally in *Cinnamon Peaks*, copyright © 1975 by The Economy Company, publishers, and the story "Rosa's Most Unforgettable Griggle" appeared originally in *Silver Twist*, copyright © 1975 by The Economy Company, publishers.

Grateful acknowledgment is made to the following for illustrations and photographs on the pages indicated:

Sue Anson 240-243, 245; Archbold Biological Station 201; The Bettmann Archive 54, 55, 342, 347, 349, 353, 355; Ellen Blonder 70, 71, 73, 230, 233, 235, 236, 239; Walter R. Courtenay, Jr. 197, 198, 202; Curt Cragg 283, 285, 287, 289; Jim Cummins 121, 123, 125, 127, 128, 206, 208, 211, 213; Darst-Ireland 45; Shelly Dietrichs 90-97; Mike Durbin 381, 384, 386, 387, 390, 393, 396, 397, 399-401, 403, 405, 408; David Fitzgerald 106, 107, 177; Elizabeth Fong 248; Susan Gilmour 24-27, 50; Barbara Hamlin 105, 247; Alma Hanson 60, 63, 65, 229; courtesy of Hollywood Turf Club 336, 340; Fran Huff 154-157, 215, 217-221, 226; Connie Hwang 326; Mary Knowles 186, 188, 189; Bob Lapsley 178, 180, 181, 183-185; courtesy of Library of Congress 53; Los Angeles Turf Club 339; Patrick Maloney 12, 14, 17, 104, 164, 166, 168-170, 172, 174, 175, 265, 268, 271; Lyle Miller 298, 302, 304, 308, 309; National Baseball Hall of Fame and Museum 314, 319; National Collection of Fine Arts, Smithsonian Institution, gift of the Harmon Foundation 250; James Needham 83, 85-87, 89; Tom Newsom 108, 113, 115, 228, 359, 363, 367, 368, 370, 371, 373, 376, 379; M. Paul Pétridès, owner 251; PGA Tour 47; Norman Prince 7, 69, 119, 223, 275; used here by permission of Ringling Bros. and Barnum & Bailey Combined Shows 8-11, 20, 22, 23, 225; Bonnie Russell 411-416, 418-428; SAH Enterprises 58; Bill Shires 141, 143, 146, 147, 151, 153, 252, 254, 256, 257, 260, 263, 292-294, 296, 297; Larry Simmons 136-140; Jeff Skrimstad 191-193, 195; Philip Smith 28, 29, 34, 35, 37, 42; Curtis Spitler 204; *Talon Inc.: A Romance of Achievement* 326-331; United Press International 323, 324; Connie Warton 131, 133, 135; Wide World Photos 47; Darrell Wiskur 99-101; Peg Zych 276, 278, 280.